Roger L. Burford
Louisiana State University

Introduction to
Finite Probability

Charles E. Merrill Books, Inc.
Columbus, Ohio

Merrill's
Mathematics and Quantitative Methods
Series

under the editorship of
Vincent E. Cangelosi
and
Melvin J. Hinich

Library of Congress Catalog Card Number: 66-29157

Printed in the United States of America

To

BETTYE, PAMELA, and ROGER MARSHALL,

who, although they do not understand,
are always understanding

Editors' Preface

This series is a new approach to the ever growing problem of providing appropriate material for basic mathematics courses offered for those planning careers in fields other than mathematics. Rapidly changing concepts in what should be offered at the undergraduate level has led to many approaches with various arrangements of topics. A serious problem arises in an effort to implement all of the material needed to satisfy the needs of these different courses. Too often there is no single book that treats the material in the desired manner or includes the desired topics at an acceptable level.

This series is planned as an integrated group of high-quality books, each complete within itself except for required background material, each covering a specified topic, and each preparing the reader for the topics that would follow naturally.

With the flexibility that such a series offers, it is hoped that every requirement can be satisfied by a careful selection of books. In designing the series, we have tried to meet two requirements. We have tried, first, to satisfy the need for flexibility in the subject material and, secondly, to present to the reader material that has been prepared by an author with a specialized background in that particular area.

In editing this series, we have insisted that each author treat his subject material in a way to give it operational meaning. With the specialist's greater familiarity in a particular subject, he can delicately merge the abstract with the practical. He can give a functional interpretation to the concepts of mathematics, thereby motivating the student and creating the necessary interest to make the learning experience exciting.

We owe a deep debt of gratitude to each author who has contributed to the series. Further, we are grateful to Charles E. Merrill Books, Inc. for the assistance they have given us in the development of this series.

Austin, Texas

Pittsburgh, Pennsylvania

Vincent E. Cangelosi

Melvin J. Hinich

Author's Preface

The purpose for writing this book is to give a thorough introduction to the theory of probability in finite sample spaces for the reader who is not majoring in mathematics or the sciences. Throughout the book, an attempt has been made to give a mathematically accurate but informal exposition of those areas of elementary probability theory which are most useful for this audience.

Throughout the book, one or more examples of application have been used following all theoretical arguments and derivations of formulas. Examples and applications have been the device used to introduce new topics of a theoretical nature. With this approach, the reader can gain a full grasp of the subject matter without becoming over burdened with material that only a mathematics and science major will need.

Since this is a finite probability book, the only mathematical background that its reader has to have can be found in the first volumes of this series — treating symbolic logic, Boolean algebra, and set theory.

Many persons' comments and suggestions have been helpful in the preparation of this manuscript. First, I am indebted to Professor Vincent Cangelosi at The University of Texas for asking me to participate in this series and for the many helpful suggestions that he gave me in various phases of manuscript completion. Also, Professors Melvin Hinich and Samuel Goldberg were very helpful for their criticisms and suggestions on mathematical presentation. I also want to thank the Charles E. Merrill Books, Inc. staff for their assistance at all stages of the project, and Mrs. Elaine Moreno, who did an excellent job in typing a rather complex manuscript. Of course, any errors of commission or omission are my responsibility.

I am greatly indebted to my wife, Bettye, and our two children for their patience and understanding while I was involved in the preparation of this manuscript.

Roger L. Burford

Contents

List of Figures

part **1**

Introduction to Probability in Finite Sample Space

chapter one

Concepts of Probability
in Finite Sample Space

It has been said that in life only death and taxes are certain. To these, we can add a third — uncertainty. This is true in all phases of life and, perhaps, especially in business. The business manager lives in an environment of uncertainty. He is uncertain of the future demand for his product, of future prices and costs, of labor supplies, and a host of other factors which have a vital effect on the success of his firm. Not only is there uncertainty about the future but about the present as well. There may be incomplete knowledge as to which of several alternative new package designs will be preferred by consumers. There may be uncertainty about which of several flavors for a new toothpaste would be preferred by consumers. Or there may be uncertainty of the chances of getting a particular contract if the necessary costs are incurred for preparation of a bid.

Probability theory is the science of uncertainty. It provides the means by which a certain amount of order and predictability may be derived from the natural state of uncertainty. Thus, a thorough under-

3

standing of the fundamentals of probability theory will permit us to deal with uncertainty in business situations in such a way that we can assess systematically the risks involved in each alternative and, consequently, act to minimize risk. We are after a means of gaining maximum "knowledge" from limited "information."

Probability, chance, odds, and *likelihood* are all words with which we are familiar. But is it always clear just what is meant when they are used? How would we interpret the statement that it isn't very *likely* to rain on a given day? Or what would we mean if we said the *odds* were against a particular horse winning a certain race? What do we mean when we say that a certain candidate will *probably* win a particular election?

In general we can say that each of these terms relates to the degree of confidence that we have in the occurrence of some event. Although the terms are not synonymous, they are generally used with the same fuzzy sort of meaning. In this book (as is usually done) we will use the term *probability* in preference to the others, and it will be given a special meaning.[1] Over the last three centuries or so, three distinctly different approaches to probability have been taken. We will discuss briefly each of these and their relative strengths and weaknesses for application to business problems.

1–1. THE CLASSICAL CONCEPT—EQUIPROBABLE EVENTS

Suppose that there are n possible outcomes to a particular experiment. If r of these possess a particular quality specified in advance (call it "success"), and if we agree in the beginning that all n possible outcomes are equally likely to occur, then we define the probability of "success" (S) to be the ratio r/n; i.e.,

$$P(S) = \frac{r}{n}.$$

---

[1] It should be noted at the outset and kept in mind throughout the work that "probability" refers always to masses or to "an individual" in general. The term never applies to a specific individual or to a specific question or proposition. A specific individual either does or does not have some characteristic, or a particular proposition either is or is not true in reality. These are not "probable." On the other hand, if it is known that a certain proportion of individuals do have some particular characteristic we can correctly speak in advance of the probability that an individual selected from the group will be one of those with that characteristic. Similarly, in the absence of knowledge of the truth or falsity of a proposition, we may speculate as to the probability of such truth or falsity.

Example 1–1

For example, suppose that we have a fish bowl containing 10 marbles all of equal size and weight. Suppose that 7 of the marbles are red and 3 are blue. Now suppose that we shake the bowl of marbles so that they are well mixed and then reach into the bowl without looking and pull out 1 marble. Since we have no reason to believe that any one marble is any more likely to be drawn than any other, and since 7 of the 10 marbles are red, we say that we are $7/10$ confident of getting a red marble. Or, in other words, the *probability* of a red marble is $7/10$ or .70.

Some writers object to this definition on grounds that, because of circularity, it really isn't a definition at all. This circularity lies in the fact that the "definition" relies on the assumption that each possible outcome is equally likely or equally probable. Hence, probability is defined in terms of probability. Because of this, it is perhaps more meaningful to think of the classical "concept" or "approach" to probability rather than thinking of this as a definition.

The classical concept of probability, which is the oldest of the concepts to be discussed, had its beginnings some three hundred years ago in Europe. The first efforts to develop probability theory were made in an attempt to provide a means of evaluating the chances of winning in various gambling games. It is easy to understand how the classical concept can apply to gambling games. All that is necessary is to determine the number of possible outcomes of a game and the number of outcomes which might result in a win or a loss.

Example 1–2

Suppose that two dice are tossed and we want to know the probability of getting any specific sum of dots on the two dice. For example, suppose we want to know the probability of getting two dots. If we assume that each of the six faces on each die is equally likely to turn up and that the two dice roll independently of one another, then each of the six faces on each die could turn up in combination with each face on the other. Hence, there are $6 \times 6 = 36$ possible outcomes on each toss. Since there is only one way of getting two dots (a single on each die), the probability of two dots is $1/36$; i.e.,

$$P(\text{Two Dots}) = \frac{1}{36}.$$

We see then that determination of probabilities according to the classical concept requires knowledge of n (the total number of possible outcomes), r (the number of outcomes called "success"), and the assumption that all n possible outcomes are equally likely. We assume a priori that the probability of "success" is equal to r/n. For business applications, these restrictions are usually much too severe. We seldom know all possible outcomes of a business venture (e.g., make $3 million profit, make $5 million profit, make $5 million loss, etc.); nor is it reasonable to assume that all of the possible outcomes are equally likely. Consequently, although the classical concept is very important in the development of probability theory, its usefulness for practical business applications is limited.

1-2. THE RELATIVE FREQUENCY CONCEPT— EMPIRICAL PROBABILITY

Suppose now that in an "experiment" comprising a large number n of repeated independent trials or observations, r of these trials result in an event or outcome S (called "success"). If n is large and the ratio r/n is near some number $p,$ and if as n becomes larger the ratio tends to approach p more closely, then we can define p to be the probability of S. Here we define a posteriori the probability of S to be the relative frequency with which the event S occurred in a long sequence of independent trials.

Example 1-3

Suppose that we would like to know the probability that a young man aged twenty-one will live to be twenty-two. If, on the basis of observation over the period of a few years, 99.8 per cent of all young men aged twenty-one have reached their twenty-second birthday, we might conclude that the probability of a twenty-one year old man living to be twenty-two is about .998. On the basis of the relative frequency approach to probability, this would indeed be our conclusion.

Example 1-4

According to the classical concept, we would say that the probability that an ordinary coin will turn up heads when tossed is .5.

We conclude this because the coin has two sides and we assume that each side is equally likely to turn up. On the other hand, suppose that we were to toss this coin independently and in the same manner a large number of times, say 1,000 times, and observe that a head turns up 440 times. From this we would conclude, by the relative frequency approach, that the probability of heads is not .5 but is approximately .44 instead. Now, suppose that we carry the experiment further by increasing the number of tosses to 10,000 and that after all these tosses we observe that 5,500 heads have turned up. We might then conclude that the probability of a head on this coin is neither .5 nor .44 but is instead approximately .55.

The point of all of this is that with the relative frequency approach we can never really know for certain the true value of p, but can only approximate it. We can, however, be fairly sure that our approximation will usually not be far off, particularly if n (the number of repetitions of the experiment) is large. It should be fairly clear that, while few real life business problems are such that all possible occurrences can be assumed realistically to be equally likely, it may very well be possible to observe the relative frequencies of occurrence of alternative possibilities. For example, suppose a business situation in which a business man is faced with the problem of how many of a particular highly perishable commodity to stock. The amount that he should stock depends on the demand for the product. As in most business situations, there is no way for the business man in this case to know all possible demands in advance, nor can he assume that all possible demands are equally likely. He may, however, be able to observe the daily demands over a fairly long period of time and construct from this a distribution of relative frequencies for no units demanded, one unit demanded, two units demanded, etc. These relative frequencies may then be interpreted as probabilities of occurrence of no demand, one unit demand, and so forth. We are assuming here, of course, that any regular variations in demand on particular days of the week and longer-run growth in demand can be taken into account separately. That is to say, demand probabilities on each day throughout the period of observation are assumed to be constant and demand on each day is assumed to be independent of demand on other days. Because observations of event-occurrences are required, the relative frequency concept is sometimes referred to as *empirical* probability.

Useful as the relative frequency concept is for practical problems, it is not difficult to conceive of problem situations to which neither the classical nor the relative frequency concept can provide a meaningful or workable solution. For example, suppose that a retailer is thinking of opening a new store in one or the other of two possible locations. Which of the two locations he should choose, if either, would depend upon the relative probabilities of success in the two locations. The problem then is how to determine these probabilities. It should be clear that the classical approach could not be applied. What are the possible outcomes in each of the two locations? Can they be considered to be equally likely? Similarly, our business man cannot use relative frequencies either. After all, he has never located a store in either of these locations, so he has no relative frequencies. Of course, it might be possible for him to assume that the relative frequencies of various outcomes from locating similar stores in sites similar to these may be used as probabilities for this problem. On the other hand, this may not be possible.

Now consider a manufacturer who has an idea for a new product. He must decide whether or not to go ahead with the development of the product and whether or not the potential gains from it are worth the effort and costs. Since the product is entirely new, there are no data available on which to determine the relative frequencies of its success or failure. Yet a decision must be made.

1–3. SUBJECTIVE PROBABILITIES

In recent years some authors have argued that the unavailability of relative frequencies or the inapplicability of the classical concept need present no insurmountable problems. They have argued that an experienced business man faced with a problem like that faced by the retailer or the manufacturer above can, on the basis of his experience with similar situations, generally assess reasonably accurately the probabilities attached to the alternatives. They argue further that two or more such experienced business men assessing the probabilities independently will usually not be far apart in their assessments.

Probability in this sense is not an objective measurable quantity. It is purely subjective and is determined by the "weight of experience." It may be thought of as a measure of the strength of one's convictions. It may be defined as the subjective feeling that some event will or will not occur, weighted by the strength of the conviction with which this feeling is held. Some authors even argue that this is really the only meaningful notion of probability.

Each of these notions of probability will be useful in particular situations, but neither of them can be used in all situations. In the following chapters we will make use of each of the concepts from time to time. In most cases the formal mathematics of probability theory will be the same regardless of which notion of probability we have in mind.

1–4. PROBABILITY AND SET THEORY

Consider a set S comprising a finite number of points (refer to a discussion of set theory). Let us then assign a weight or number to each of the points in S such that the sum of the weights assigned is 1 and such that each weight is between 0 and 1. The weights may be interpreted as probabilities of occurrence of each point. Now consider a subset A of S, i.e., $A \subseteq S$. The probability measure of A on S is then given by the sum of the weights of all of those points in S which are also in A. Similarly, for other subsets, B, C, etc. of S we can also define probability measures. We can then apply to our measures of probability all of the operations on sets covered in a treatment of set theory. This will enable us to analyze compound probabilities in much the same way that compound statements were analyzed there. Consider, for example, the set S of all students at your college or university. Clearly S comprises many subsets. There is the subset M of males and the subset F of females. There is the subset J of juniors, the subset B of blonds, and the subset C of "C students" and many more. We will be able to use set notations to express the joint and compound probabilities of various combinations of these subsets simultaneously. In much of the rest of the book we will make use of the notation and methodology of sets. It should be noted that this way of treating probability is conceptually the same as the classical concept.

CONCEPTS TO THINK ABOUT

Probability	Subjective Probability
Likelihood	Equiprobable Events
Odds	Relative Frequency
Chance	Empirical Probability
A priori	Proportion
Objective Probability	*A posteriori*

Selected References

Feller, W., *Introduction to Probability Theory and Its Applications*, Vol. I, 2nd. ed., New York: John Wiley & Sons, Inc., 1957.

Goldberg, S., *Probability — An Introduction*, Englewood Cliffs, N. J.: Prentice-Hall, Inc., 1962.

Schlaifer, R., *Probability and Statistics for Business Decisions*, New York: McGraw-Hill Book Company, Inc., 1959.

Uspensky, J. V., *Introduction to Mathematical Probability*, New York: McGraw-Hill Book Company, Inc., 1937.

chapter two

Fundamental Theorems
of Probability

2–1. SOME BASIC CONCEPTS

In this chapter we will examine in some detail the main body of what is frequently referred to as the probability calculus. We are interested here in rules by which we can combine probabilities of *elementary events* in order to determine probabilities of more complex or *compound events*. It is customary to refer to any process of observation in business as an experiment. An *event* is an outcome of an experiment or a result of a trial or an observation. For example, if we toss a single coin, there are two possible events, head and tail. These are *elementary events*. Similarly, a toss of two coins may result in four elementary events; a head on both coins, a head on the first coin and a tail on the second, a tail on the first and a head on the second, and a tail on both coins. The probabilities of each of these elementary events are the same (according to the classical concept), $\frac{1}{4}$. From these elementary events we can determine the probabilities of several

11

compound events. For example, the probability of exactly one head is the sum of the probabilities of the two events consisting of exactly one head. Hence, the probability of exactly one head is ½. In the language of sets, the set S of outcomes in this case comprises four points (*HH, HT, TH, TT*). In this example we have assigned each of these four points equal weights. Hence, the point *HH* is given a weight of ¼ as is each of the other points. Hence, the probability of exactly one head is defined as the sum of the weights attached to each of the two points, *HT* and *TH*. That is, we define

$$P(\text{one Head}) = \frac{1}{4} + \frac{1}{4} = \frac{1}{2}.$$

In general, the sum of the weights assigned to each of the points in the finite set S must be equal to 1, and we may interpret the weights assigned to the individual points as probabilities of their occurrence.

Example 2–1

Suppose now we have a bag containing 10 marbles of which 7 marbles are red and 3 are white. Suppose further that all of the marbles are of equal size and weight so that if they are mixed well there will be no tendency for certain ones to rise to the top or sink to the bottom. Now suppose that we conduct an experiment in which we select one marble from the bag, record its color, and replace it in the bag. There are altogether ten possible elementary events that could result from this experiment, one corresponding to each of the ten marbles. It would be possible to define many different compound events from the results of this experiment. For example, in a sequence of three drawings one compound event might consist of all possible such sequences comprising one white and two red marbles.

The notion of an event is of central importance in probability and the solution of all exercises in this chapter will require that the student have a clear understanding of just what comprises the event or events of the problem. Perhaps a clearer conception of events will develop as we proceed.

2–2. THE NATURE OF PROBABILITY

In each of the definitions of probability presented in the first chapter we referred to a probability as a ratio. In the case of the classical concept we said that the probability of a particular event E is the ratio of the number of ways in which that event can occur to the number of possible outcomes. If r is the number of ways that E can occur and n is the number of possible outcomes, then the probability of E is

$$P(E) = \frac{r}{n}.$$

Similarly, by the relative frequency concept, if out of a long series n of trials, the event E occurs r times, then we say that the probability of E is approximately

$$P(E) \cong \frac{r}{n}.[1]$$

It should be clear that in either of these cases the following condition must hold:

$$0 \le P(E) \le 1.$$

This is true because

$$0 \le r \le n.$$

Now, how do we interpret the extremes of the probability range? What does $P(E) = 0$ mean? And what does $P(E) = 1$ mean? The answers to these questions depend on which concept of probability we have in mind. If we are thinking of the classical concept, $P(E) = 0$ means that the event is impossible; it cannot occur. On the other hand, by the relative frequency concept, $P(E) = 0$ does not necessarily mean that the event is impossible, but simply that it has not occurred during the conduct of the experiment. Similarly, by the classical concept, $P(E) = 1$ means that the event is absolutely certain. By the relative frequency concept this means only that it has occurred on all of the trials so far.

The probability of an event, then, can be interpreted as the proportion of times in a long series of repeated trials that the event can be expected to occur. On a given trial the event either will or will not occur and cannot really be said to be probable as such. A probability interpretation can be given in that we can ask what is the probability that this trial will be one of those resulting in the event E.

2–3. COUNTING SCHEMES

Thus far we have defined the probability of an event E as the ratio of two numbers r and n, where r is defined as the number of possible

---

[1]The notation $\cong$ is used here to mean "approximately equal to."

outcomes of an experiment which are such that the event E occurs and n is the total number of possible outcomes. It is necessary, therefore, to be able to determine the values of r and n. This may be done in many cases by some rather sophisticated counting schemes, which will be discussed here.

Suppose that we begin with the very simple situation in which we are about to toss an ordinary coin which, being an ordinary coin, has a "head" on one side and a "tail" on the other. We would like to know the total number of possible outcomes of a toss of this coin. Clearly, there are only two possible outcomes which can be given serious consideration; namely, a head or a tail. We can safely disregard the possibility that the coin will stand on its edge. Now let us suppose that, instead of tossing a single coin, we toss two. Now how many outcomes are there? This question can be answered by reference to the tree diagram in Figure 2–1. From Figure 2–1, it is clear that each coin has two possible outcomes and that each of the two outcomes on the first coin can appear in combination with each of the outcomes on the second. The possible sequences of heads and tails on the two coins are, then, $HH, HT, TH,$ and $TT.$ Another, more succinct way of looking at the problem is to note that there are two ways that each of the coins can turn up and that the outcome on the first has no effect on the outcome on the second, and vice versa. Hence, each of the two outcomes on the first coin can occur with each of the two on the second. Therefore, the total number of outcomes (n) is

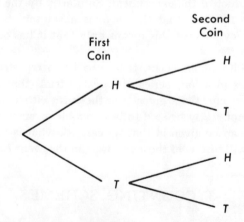

FIGURE 2–1. Tree Diagram of the Outcomes on a Toss of Two Coins

given by $n = 2 \times 2$. Similarly, if there are three coins, the total number of outcomes would be $n = 2 \times 2 \times 2$, or $n = 2^3$. In general, if we toss some number w of coins, the total number of possible outcomes would be $n = 2^w$.

Suppose now that, instead of coins, we toss a pair of dice and we want to know the number of possible outcomes. In this case, the number of outcomes on each die is six; moreover, the outcome on each die is *independent* of the outcome on the other, a concept we will discuss in detail in 2–6. Each of the six faces on die one can combine with each of the six faces on die two, so that the number of outcomes on the two together would be $n = 6 \times 6$, or $n = 6^2$. If we had three dice, the number of possible outcomes would be $n = 6^3$. Similarly, if we had w dice, the number of possible outcomes of a toss would be $n = 6^w$.

What we have been saying with respect to coins and dice can now be said in more general terms. Namely, if we conduct an experiment comprising w trials such that the outcome on each trial is independent of the outcomes on each of the other trials, and such that on each trial there are m possible outcomes, then the total number of outcomes of the experiment is

$$n = m^w. \tag{2-1}$$

In the case of the coins above, $m = 2$. In the case of the dice $m = 6$.

Example 2–2

Suppose for example that we have written the 26 letters of the alphabet on 26 cards (one letter per card). Now suppose that we shuffle the deck well and select a card, replace the card, shuffle and select another card, and continue this process of selecting a card, replacing, shuffling, and selecting again until six cards have been selected. How many different sequences of six letters could we select? In this case, $m = 26$ and $w = 6$. Hence, the number of possible six-letter sequences is $n = 26^6$, an extremely large number.

Let us now consider a somewhat different sort of problem from those that we have discussed so far in this section. In each of the problems posed so far we have assumed that the outcomes on each trial were the same from trial to trial. Let us now drop this assumption and see how this affects the number of outcomes of the experiment. Suppose that the experiment to be undertaken is such that the number of possible outcomes on the first trial is m_1, the number on the second (given that the first trial has taken place) is m_2, the number on the third trial is m_3, and so on. Then the total number of possible outcomes of w trials is

$$n = m_1 \cdot m_2 \cdot m_3 \cdot m_4 \ldots m_w. \qquad (2\text{-}2)$$

Actually, Equation 2-2 is more general than Equation 2-1, and includes Equation 2-1 as a special case where $m_1 = m_2 = m_3 = \ldots .$ $= m_w = m$. Equation 2-2 also has many other special cases, some of which we will take up now.

Let us suppose that we are to conduct an experiment which consists of arranging m objects in sequence. How many possible outcomes are there to this experiment? Each different possible sequence or *permutation* of the m objects constitutes a different outcome. The first position in the sequence could be occupied by any one of the m objects. However, given that one object has been selected for the first position, there are only $m-1$ left for the second position. Similarly, once selections have been made for both the first and the second positions, there are only $m-2$ objects left which could be put into the third. Then, for the fourth position, there are only $m-3$, for the fifth position there are only $m-4$, and so on until for the mth position there is only one. Since any one of the m objects could be in the first position, any one of the remaining $m-1$ in the second, and so on, the repeated application of Equation 2-2 to this problem gives

$$n = m \cdot (m-1) \cdot (m-2) \cdot (m-3) \ldots 3 \cdot 2 \cdot 1. \ (2\text{-}3)$$

Here m is the same as m_1 in Equation 2-2, $m-1$ is the value of m_2, $m-2$ is the value of m_3, and so forth. As a "shorthand" way of stating Equation 2-3, we will follow the convention of the following definition:

$$m! = m \cdot (m-1) \cdot (m-2) \ldots 3 \cdot 2 \cdot 1. \qquad (2\text{-}4)$$

We call $m!$ *m factorial* and it may be interpreted as the number of arrangements or *permutations* of m objects among themselves. It should be noted that $1! = 1$, and that we *define* $0! = 1$. Some examples might be helpful.

Example 2–3

How many sequences of the letters of the alphabet are possible? In arranging the letters in sequence, any one of 26 letters could be selected for the first position. Once a letter is selected for the first position, any one of 25 could be selected for the second position. Then any one of the remaining 24 could be selected for the third position, and so on. Hence, the answer to the question is the following product:

$$n = 26! = 26 \times 25 \times 24 \times 23 \cdots 3 \times 2 \times 1.$$

Example 2–4

How many different ways can ten men line themselves up in a row? In this case $n = 10! = 10 \times 9 \times 8 \times 7 \times 6 \times 5 \times 4 \times 3 \times 2 \times 1$.

Suppose now that we would like to know the number of permutations of x objects from among m. That is to say, we want to know the number of ways that we can select x objects from m. For example, how many three-letter "words" can we select from the alphabet not allowing repetition of letters? Clearly, the first of the three letters could be any one of the 26 in the alphabet. The second could be any one of 25 letters, given that a letter has been selected for the first position. The third letter could be any one of the remaining 24. Hence, the number of permutations is equal to $26 \times 25 \times 24$. Let us note now that $26! = 26 \times 25 \times 24 \times 23!$, so that $26 \times 25 \times 24 = 26!/23!$. In general, the number of *permutations of x objects selected from m* is

$$_mP_r = m \cdot (m - 1) \cdot (m - 2) \cdots (m - x + 1),$$

or

$$_mP_r = \frac{m!}{(m - x)!}. \qquad (2-5)$$

Consider the following example.

Example 2–5

How many different five-card sequences could be dealt from an ordinary well shuffled deck of playing cards? Here the first card dealt could be any one of 52, the second any one of the remaining 51, the third any one of the remaining 50, the fourth any one of 49, and the fifth any one of 48. Hence, the number of possible five-card sequences is

$$_{52}P_5 = 52 \times 51 \times 50 \times 49 \times 48 = \frac{52!}{47!}.$$

Example 2–6

Suppose now that we would like to know how many different seven-digit numbers we can form by rearranging the following digits: 1, 2, 1, 3, 4, 2, 1. Clearly, there are 7! permutations of the digits among themselves, but not all of these constitute different numbers. There are three ones, and all of the possible permutations of these are identical. Similarly, all of the permutations of the two twos are also identical. Hence, the number of *distinguishable* permutations of the seven digits is $7!/(3! \times 2!)$. There are 3! permutations of the three ones and 2! permutations of the two twos. Each of these permutations is identical. The number of different numbers that can be formed is the same as the number of distinguishable permutations. In this case, there are 420.

We can now generalize the result of Example 2–6. We want to know the number of permutations of m objects which are such that w are identical to each other, x are identical to each other, y are identical to each other, z are identical to each other, etc., but that the w objects are different from all others, the x are different from others, the y are different from others, the z are different from others, etc. Now, the number of *distinguishable* permutations (assuming that $w + x + y + z \dots = m$) is

$$_mP_{w,x,y,z,\dots} = \frac{m!}{w!\, x!\, y!\, z! \dots} \tag{2–6}$$

Let us now consider a related but somewhat different problem. In many instances we may be interested in determining the number of ways of selecting x objects from among a larger group, but the particular sequence or order of selection may *not* be important. The problem posed here is similar to the one in the development of Equation 2–5. However, there we were interested in the number of *sequences* of x objects which may be selected from among m. The number of possible selections *ignoring* order of selection should be less than the number of possible orders of selection. "How much smaller?" is the question to be answered here. Really, this is quite simple. We know already that the number of sequences or permutations of x objects selected from m is $_mP_x$ as defined in Equation 2–5. Since we are not concerned here about the order of selection of the x objects, we can just divide the number of arrangements of the x objects. That is to say, the number of *combinations* of x objects selected from m (defined as the number of permutations disregarding the order of those selected) is

$$\binom{m}{x} = \frac{_mP_x}{x!} \cdot$$

or

$$\binom{m}{x} = \frac{m!}{x!\,(m-x)!} \cdot \qquad (2\text{-}7)$$

The $\binom{m}{x}$ notation has come to be rather standard. Some authors write this as C_x^m and others as $_mC_x$. However, the $\binom{m}{x}$ notation (read the number of *combinations* of x objects selected from m) is used most frequently in recent books and will be used throughout this book. An example of application of Equation 2–7 will be helpful.

Example 2–7

The number of possible five-card poker hands that can be dealt from an ordinary deck of playing cards is

$$\binom{52}{5} = \frac{52!}{5!\,47!} = \frac{52 \times 51 \times 50 \times 49 \times 48}{5 \times 4 \times 3 \times 2 \times 1} = 2{,}598{,}960.$$

In the case of card hands, we use the formula for combinations because the order of selection of the cards is of no importance. The particular *collection* of cards dealt is important, but *not their order.*

Computations using Equation 2–7 are frequently very tedious. In order to facilitate computations somewhat, values of $\binom{m}{x}$ for m up to 20 are included in Appendix Table II. It can be confirmed from the table that, for example, $\binom{17}{9} = 24{,}310$. The values of m are indicated in the left margin of the table and the values of x are given in the headings. It should be noted that $\binom{m}{x}$ is defined only if $x \leq m$. It is important to note also that $\binom{m}{x} = \binom{m}{m-x}$ for all $x \leq m$. The student can verify this easily for himself.

2–4. PROBABILITIES OF MUTUALLY EXCLUSIVE EVENTS

Consider the events A and B as depicted in Figure 2–2. Here, events A and B are said to be *mutually exclusive* and *collectively exhaustive*. That is, one or the other A or B must occur but they cannot both occur at the same time. As indicated earlier, the sum of the probabilities of mutually exclusive and exhaustive events is equal to 1. Suppose that A denotes the occurrence of a six on the toss of a die, and B denotes the occurrence of any face other than a six. Then it follows that

$$P(A) = 1 - P(B). \tag{2–8}$$

B is the *complement* of A. This property of probabilities is frequently very useful for computational purposes. In the example above we could determine the probability of not getting a six (the probability of B) in one of two ways. We could add the probabilities of each of the other five faces, or we could simply subtract the probability of six from one; namely,

$$P(B) = 1 - P(A) = 1 - \frac{1}{6} = \frac{5}{6}.$$

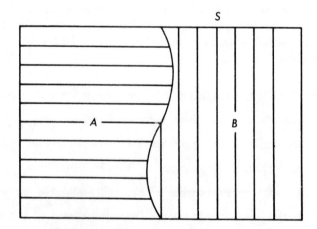

FIGURE 2–2. Partition of Set S into Mutually Exclusive and Exhaustive Subsets A and B

Suppose now that we would like to know the probability of getting more than two dots on the toss of a pair of dice. It should be clear that two dots can turn up in only one way, a one on each of the two dice. Moreover, there are altogether $6^2 = 36$ possible outcomes on a toss of two dice. That is, each of the two dice has six faces and each of the six faces can turn up in combination with each of the others. Therefore, the probability of getting two dots (call this the event A) is $\frac{1}{36}$. Then the probability of getting more than two dots (call this the event B) is

$$P(B) = 1 - P(A) = 1 - \frac{1}{36} = \frac{35}{36}.$$

Also, it should be noted again that

$$P(A) + P(B) = 1. \tag{2-9}$$

Now, suppose that our two events A and B are mutually exclusive but are not collectively exhaustive. They may be depicted as in Figure 2–3. Here it is possible that neither A nor B will occur. Suppose now that we would like to know the probability that either A or B will occur. To gain a clear understanding of this probability, think of A and B in Figure 2–3 as disjoint subsets of the set S. Suppose that S comprises n equally likely elements and that the subsets A and B comprise n_a and n_b elements each respectively. Suppose there are n_c elements that are neither A nor B. Then

$$P(A \text{ or } B) = P(A \cup B) = \frac{(n_a + n_b)}{n},$$

where

$$n = n_a + n_b + n_c.$$

Thus,

$$P(A \cup B) = \frac{n_a}{n} + \frac{n_b}{n}$$

or

$$P(A \cup B) = P(A) + P(B). \tag{2-10}$$

Although Equation 2–10 has been proved only for the case of equally likely sample points, it holds for other cases as well.

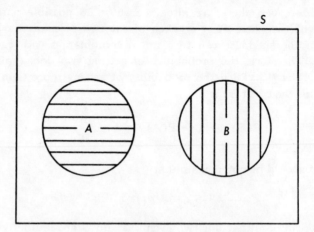

**FIGURE 2–3. Partition of Set S into Mutu-
ally Exclusive but not Ex-
haustive Subsets A and B**

Example 2–8

Let us look now at the set of all possible outcomes of a toss
of a pair of ordinary dice. These possible outcomes are shown
in Figure 2-4. Altogether there are 36 possible elementary events,
or elements in the *universe set S*. Each die has 6 faces, and the
6 faces of each can combine with each of the 6 faces of the
other. This will perhaps be clearer if we think of 1 die as being
red and the other as green. If we now define subsets of *S* according to the sum of dots on the 2 dice, we can see from Figure 2–4
that there are 11 mutually exclusive or disjoint sets corresponding to the cases where there are 2 dots, 3 dots, 4 dots, and so
on to 12 dots. If *X* is the number of dots on the 2 dice, *r* is the
number of elements in the subset corresponding to *X*, and 36 is
total number of outcomes of a toss (elements in the universe
set), then

$$P(X) = \frac{r}{36}.$$

Thus, the probability that $X = 2$ is $\frac{1}{36}$, the probability that $X = 3$

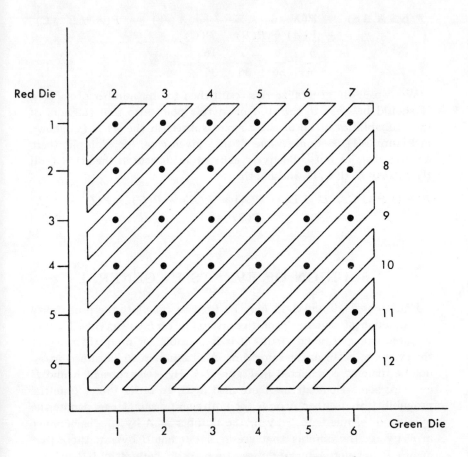

**FIGURE 2–4. 36 Outcomes of a Toss of
Two Dice**

is $\frac{2}{36}$, the probability that $X = 7$ is $\frac{6}{36}$, and so on. Now suppose
that we want to know the probability that either six or seven dots
will turn up. If we apply Equation 2–3 to this, we can refer to the
event $X = 6$ as the subset A and to the event $X = 7$ assign the
letter B. Then,

$$P(X=6 \ \cup \ X=7) = P(A \cup B) = P(A) + P(B)$$
$$= \frac{5}{36} + \frac{6}{36} = \frac{11}{36}.$$

Now, if we refer to the event $X = 8$ as the subset C, it should be clear that

$$P(6 \leq X \leq 8) = P(X=6 \ \cup \ X=7 \ \cup \ X=8) = P(A \cup B \cup C)$$
$$= P(A) + P(B) + P(C)$$
$$= \frac{5}{36} + \frac{6}{36} + \frac{5}{36} = \frac{16}{36}.$$

We can easily generalize this result then to any number of subsets. It should be clear to the student at this point also that the sum of the probabilities of all of the disjoint subsets in the set S (as shown in Figure 2–4) is equal to one. If in a given case, for example, there are five disjoint but collectively exhaustive subsets in the set S (call the subsets $A, B, C, D, and E$), then

$$P(A \cup B \cup C \cup D \cup E) = P(A) + P(B) + P(C) + P(D) + P(E)$$
$$= P(S) = 1. \qquad (2-11)$$

2–5. UNION OF EVENTS IN GENERAL

Equations 2–10 and 2–11 may be used to calculate the probability of the union of several *disjoint* or *mutually exclusive* events. Neither of these will give valid results if it is possible for more than one of the events to occur at the same time. A situation in which subsets may not be disjoint is depicted in Figure 2-5. Here the subsets A and B overlap; some elements in A are also in B. In order to evaluate the probability that either A or B (or both) will occur, let us denote the number of elements in S by n; the number in A by n_a; the number in B by n_b; the number that are in A but not B by $n_{a\bar{b}}$; those that are in B but not A by $n_{\bar{a}b}$; those that are in both A and B by n_{ab}; and those that are neither in A nor B by $n_{\bar{a}\bar{b}}$. Here, $n_a = n_{ab} + n_{a\bar{b}}$, $n_b = n_{ab} + n_{\bar{a}b}$, and $n = n_{ab} + n_{a\bar{b}} + n_{\bar{a}b} + n_{\bar{a}\bar{b}}$. Thus, (assuming the n elements to be equally likely),

$$P(A \cup B) = \frac{(n_{ab} + n_{a\bar{b}} + n_{\bar{a}b})}{n}$$
$$= \frac{(n_{a\bar{b}} + n_{ab} + n_{\bar{a}b} + n_{ab} - n_{ab})}{n}$$
$$= \frac{(n_{a\bar{b}} + n_{ab})}{n} + \frac{(n_{\bar{a}b} + n_{ab})}{n} - \frac{n_{ab}}{n}$$
$$= P(A) + P(B) - P(A \cap B). \qquad (2-12)$$

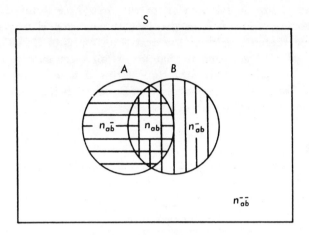

FIGURE 2–5. Partition of Set S into Non-exclusive Subsets A and B

In Equation 2–12, $P(A \cap B)$ is interpreted as the probability that both A and B will occur; $(A \cap B)$ is the intersection of the two subsets A and B. The reason for subtracting $P(A \cap B)$ in Equation 2–12 is that the probabilities $P(A)$ and $P(B)$ both include $P(A \cap B)$. That is, each element in the subsets A and B *should* be included as a contribution to the probability $P(A \cup B)$ once and only once. However, without the subtraction of $P(A \cap B)$ in Equation 2–12, the elements n_{ab} would be included twice. It should be noted that Equation 2–12 is more general than Equation 2–10. This is clearly the case since in the situation depicted in Figure 2-3 there is no overlap of A and B, so $n_{ab} = 0$. In this case Equations 2–10 and 2–12 yield the same result.

Suppose now that we are interested in the probability of one or more of three events A, B, and C as depicted in Figure 2–6. By a similar analysis to that used to derive Equation 2–12, it can be shown that

$$P(A \cup B \cup C) = P(A) + P(B) + P(C) - P(A \cap B) - P(A \cap C)$$
$$- P(B \cap C) + P(A \cap B \cap C). \qquad (2\text{–}13)$$

Equation 2–13 will become intuitively clear if we observe that the first three terms on the right side include all of the elements twice that are both A and B but not C. Similarly, all of those elements that are A and C but not B are included twice, as are all of the elements that are *B* and *C* but not *A*. All of the elements that are *A, B, and C* are included in all of the first three terms. Now, the double counting involved in the first three terms is corrected by subtracting these elements in the next three terms of Equation 2–13. However, all of the elements that are in all three subsets are subtracted three times in the next three terms. Finally, these elements are added back once in the last term of Equation 2–13. The derivation of Equation 2–13 will be left as an exercise.

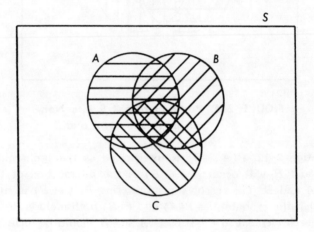

FIGURE 2–6. Partition of Set S into Non-exclusive Subsets A, B, and C

Example 2–9

Let us consider a group of 100 students with the following characteristics: 40 of them are enrolled in the school of business, 25 are taking a course in statistics, and 10 have overall grade averages of B or better. Suppose further that 20 of the business students are taking a course in statistics, 3 of the business students have grade averages of B or better, 4 of the 25 students taking statistics have grade averages of B or better, and 2 business students who are taking statistics have a grade average of B or better. Suppose that we select 1 student at random from the 100 and we want to know the probability that we will select a student who is either a business student, is enrolled in a course in statistics, or who has a grade average of B or better. Let us define the event "business student" as A, taking statistics as B, and has a grade of B or better as C. Then by Equation 2–13,

$$P(A \cup B \cup C) = .40 + .25 + .10 - .20 - .03 - .04 + .02$$
$$= .50 .$$

In the application of Equation 2–13 it is necessary that not only the probabilities of A, B, C, etc. be known individually, but also that the *joint* probabilities of A and B, A and C, B and C, etc. be known as well. These are not always known, but we may frequently have information by which they may be determined. In the next two sections we will be interested in the determination of these probabilities.

2–6. INDEPENDENCE AND THE INTERSECTION OF EVENTS

Two events are said to be *stochastically independent,* or just *independent,* if the occurrence or nonoccurrence of one of them has no effect on the probability of occurrence of the other. For example, suppose that we toss two coins. The outcome on the second coin is not affected by the outcome on the first, or vice versa. The two events (the outcomes on the first and second tosses) are independent. If we toss a pair of dice, the outcome on the second die is unaffected by the outcome on the first, and vice versa. If we have ten marbles in a fish bowl and draw marbles from the bowl one at a time and replace the marble each time before the next selection, then the outcome on each selection is independent. If and only if the two events are independent, then

$$P(A \cap B) = P(A) \cdot P(B) . \qquad (2-14)$$

At this point we cannot prove Equation 2–14. We will, however, return to this in the next section.

The probability of any particular sequence of outcomes on a toss of two coins is $(.5) \times (.5) = .25$. If we draw two marbles from a fish bowl containing six red and four white marbles, replacing after each draw, the probability of getting two red marbles is $(.6) \times (.6) = .36$. The probability of getting a red marble and then a white one is $(.6) \times (.4) = .24$. Now, it should be noted that two events A and B cannot be both *independent* and *mutually exclusive* at the same time. If they are mutually exclusive, they cannot occur at the same time; the occurrence of one precludes the occurrence of the other. If events A and B are mutually exclusive, the occurrence of A means that the probability of B is zero. Hence, "head" and "tail" on the same toss of a coin are mutually exclusive and, therefore, not independent. However, the occurrence of head on one coin has no effect on the outcome of any other coin. The outcomes of the two or more coins are independent but not mutually exclusive. In this case $P(H) = \frac{1}{2}$ and $P(T) = \frac{1}{2}$. However, since the two events are mutually exclusive,

$$P(H \cap T) = 0 \neq P(H) \cdot P(T) = \frac{1}{4}.$$

The fact that two events A and B are not mutually exclusive, however, does not necessarily mean that they are independent. For example, the color of a person's hair and the color of his eyes are certainly not mutually exclusive, but neither are they independent. It is more likely that a person with dark hair will also have dark eyes than that he will have blue eyes. The treatment of probabilities for nonindependent events will be taken up momentarily but, in the meantime, we can generalize Equation 2–14 to determine the joint probability of occurrence of any number n of independent events, A_1, A_2, A_3, ..., A_n, as follows

$$P(A_i \cap A_j) = P(A_i) \cdot P(A_j), \ (1 \leq i < j \leq n)$$
$$P(A_i \cap A_j \cap A_k) = P(A_i) \cdot P(A_j) \cdot P(A_k), \ (1 \leq i < j < k \leq n)$$
$$\cdot \ \cdot$$
$$\cdot \ \cdot$$
$$P(A_1 \cap A_2 \cap \ldots \cap A_n) = P(A_1) \cdot P(A_2) \ldots P(A_n). \qquad (2\text{--}15)$$

That is to say, n events are jointly independent if and only if the multiplication rule holds for all combinations of two or more of the events.

Example 2–10

Suppose that we draw four marbles (replacing after each draw) from a fish bowl containing two red, two white, four black, and two green marbles. The probability that we will draw a red, a black, a white, and a green marble, in that order, is

$$(.2) \times (.4) \times (.2) \times (.2) = .0016.$$

2-7. NONINDEPENDENCE AND CONDITIONAL PROBABILITY

Consider two events A and B. Say A is the event that an individual has annual income of $10,000 a year or more, and B is the event that he is a college graduate. Suppose we know that the probability that an individual selected at random from a particular population has income of $10,000 a year or more is .44. Suppose also that we know that the probability of an individual having a college education is .52. Given that we know that a particular individual has a college education, we want to know the probability that he has income of $10,000 or more. If A and B were independent, this would be simply $P(A) = .44$. However, we have reason to believe that income and education are not independent. A person with a college education is more likely to have income over $10,000 than is a person with less than a college education. Actually, we don't have enough information yet to determine the probability that we are after. If, however, we know that 30 per cent of the people in this population have both a college education and an income of $10,000 a year or more, we would be in a position to determine the *conditional* probability of A given that B has occurred. Namely,

$$P(A|B) = \frac{.30}{.52} = .58 .$$

To see how this result was derived look at Figure 2-7. Here, we are asking simply what is the proportion of B which is also A. In effect, we have redefined the universe set to be the subset B and are asking the probability that an event which is B is also A. Figure 2-7 depicts a situation similar to that in Figure 2-5. The main difference is that we have assigned specific values to n_{ab}/n, $n_{a\bar{b}}/n$, etc. In Figure 2-7, $n_{ab}/n = .30$; $n_{a\bar{b}}/n = .52$; and $n_{\bar{a}\bar{b}}/n = .66$. Stated in terms of the n's rather than in specific numeric values as above,

$$P(A|B) = \frac{n_{ab}}{n_{ab} + n_{\bar{a}b}} = \frac{n_{ab}}{n_{ab} + n_{\bar{a}b}} \cdot \frac{n}{n}$$

$$= \frac{\dfrac{n_{ab}}{n}}{\dfrac{n_{ab} + n_{\bar{a}b}}{n}} .$$

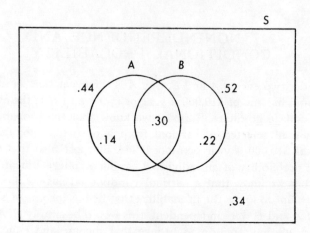

FIGURE 2–7. Probability Measures for Non-
exclusive Subsets A and B

But n_{ab}/n is the probability of both A and B and $(n_{ab} + n_{\bar{a}b})/n$ is the probability of B without regard to whether or not A occurs. Hence,

$$P(A|B) = \frac{P(A \cap B)}{P(B)}.$$

$\qquad$ (2–16)

Similarly,

$$P(B|A) = \frac{P(A \cap B)}{P(A)}.$$

$\qquad$ (2–16a)

And from these we can see that

$$P(A \cap B) = P(A) \cdot P(B|A) = P(B) \cdot P(A|B).$$ (2–17)

Equations 2–16, 2–16a, and 2–17 are much more general than Equation 2–14 in that they are applicable even where the events A and B are actually independent, in addition to the cases where A and B are dependent. This should be easy to see since if the events A and B are independent, then

$$P(A|B) = P(A), \text{ and } P(B|A) = P(B).$$

At this point we can easily provide the promised proof of Equation 2–14. Since, if A and B are independent $P(A|B) = P(A)$ and $P(B|A) = P(B)$, substitution into Equation 2–17 yields Equation 2–14 immediately.

Example 2–11

Consider again the problem of selecting two marbles from a fish bowl containing six red and four white marbles. This time, however, suppose that we draw the two marbles *without* replacing the first one before the second selection is made. We want to know the probability of selecting two red marbles. This problem

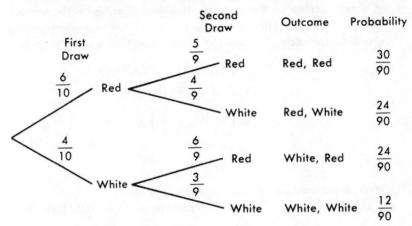

FIGURE 2–8. Outcomes of Selection of Two Marbles from a Fishbowl

is illustrated in Figure 2–8. Clearly, the probability of a red marble on the first draw is, as before, $6/10$. However, if a red marble is drawn on the first draw, the probability of a red on the second is no longer $6/10$ as it was when selection was with replacement. Now the probability of a red on the second selection is only $5/9$. That is, there are only nine marbles left in the fish bowl after the first selection and, given that a red marble was drawn on the first draw, there are only five red ones left. Thus, the probability of a red marble on both the first and second selections is $(6/10) \times (5/9) = 30/90 = 1/3$, as contrasted with $(.6) \times (.6) = .36$ if the first marble is replaced before the second selection is made. Hence, if we define the occurrence of a red marble on the first selection to be the event A and a red on the second selection to be B, then the probability of both A and B is

$$P(A \cap B) = P(A) \cdot P(B|A) = \left(\frac{6}{10}\right) \cdot \left(\frac{5}{9}\right) = \frac{1}{3}.$$

Example 2–12

Let's modify the problem of the last example slightly and ask simply what is the probability of getting exactly one red marble on a selection of two marbles from the fish bowl (without replacement)? Here we are really asking for the probability of a compound event comprising two elementary events; (1) the occurrence of a red marble on the first selection and a white on the second, and (2) the occurrence of a white marble on the first selection and a red on the second. Thus, the probability that we are after is

$$P(A \cup B) = P(A \cap \bar{B}) + P(\bar{A} \cap B)$$
$$= P(A) \cdot P(\bar{B}|A) + P(\bar{A}) \cdot P(B|\bar{A})$$
$$= \left(\frac{6}{10}\right) \times \left(\frac{4}{9}\right) + \left(\frac{4}{10}\right) \times \left(\frac{6}{9}\right)$$
$$= \frac{24}{45}.$$

Here, $\bar{B}$ means "not B" and $\bar{A}$ means "not A."
If the selections had been with replacement, this would have been

$$2\left(\frac{6}{10}\right) \times \left(\frac{4}{10}\right) = \frac{24}{50} = \frac{12}{25}.$$

Let us now extend Equation 2–17 to the general case where we want to know the joint probability of occurrences of n events, $A_1, A_2, \dots A_n$. That is to say, we want to know $P(A_1 \cap A_2 \cap \dots \cap A_n)$. To this end, let us note that

$$P(A_1 \cap A_2) = P(A_1) \cdot P(A_2|A_1).$$

Moreover, if we define the event B to be the joint occurrence of A_1 and A_2 (i.e., $B = A_1 \cap A_2$) then

$$P(B \cap A_3) = P(B) \cdot P(A_3|B)$$

or equivalently,

$$P(A_1 \cap A_2 \cap A_3) = P(A_1 \cap A_2) \cdot P(A_3|A_1 \cap A_2)$$
$$= P(A_1) \cdot P(A_2|A_1) \cdot P(A_3|A_1 \cap A_2).$$

Following this same reasoning, it can be shown that

$$P(A_1 \cap A_2 \cap A_3 \cap \dots \cap A_n) = P(A_1) \cdot P(A_2|A_1) \cdot P(A_3|A_1 \cap A_2)$$
$$\dots \cdot P(A_n|A_1 \cap A_2 \cap \dots A_{n-1}). \qquad (2\text{–}18)$$

Example 2–13

To illustrate, if we select four marbles from our fish bowl containing six red and four white marbles, the probability that we will draw first two white and then two red marbles, given that we drew two white ones (again assuming that selections are made in sequence without replacement after each selection) is

$$\left(\frac{4}{10}\right) \times \left(\frac{3}{9}\right) \times \left(\frac{6}{8}\right) \times \left(\frac{5}{7}\right) = \frac{360}{5040} = \frac{9}{126}.$$

Here, $\frac{4}{10}$ is the probability of a white marble on the first selection; $\frac{3}{9}$ is the conditional probability of a white on the second selection, given that a white was drawn on the first; $\frac{6}{8}$ is the probability of a red marble on the third selection, given that whites were drawn on the first two; and $\frac{5}{7}$ is the conditional probability of a red on the fourth draw, given that whites were drawn on the first two and a red on the third.

To summarize what has been covered so far in this chapter, let us put the information in Figure 2–7 into another form in Figure 2–9.

	A	$\overline{A}$	Total
B	.30	.22	.52
$\overline{B}$	.14	.34	.48
Total	.44	.56	1.00

FIGURE 2–9. Table of Probabilities for Events A and B

From this tabular form we can determine a number of different probabilities relating to events A and B directly and can easily determine many others with a little calculation. Such a table can be of considerable help in calculating various probabilities. For example $P(A \cap B) = .30, P(\overline{A} \cap B) = .22, P(A \cap \overline{B}) = .14, P(\overline{A} \cap \overline{B}) = .34, P(A) = .44, P(\overline{A}) = 1 - P(A) = .56, P(B) = .52, P(\overline{B}) = 1 - P(B) = .48$. All of these probabilities were read directly from the table. It should be noted that $P(A)$, $P(B)$, $P(\overline{A})$, and $P(\overline{B})$ are called *marginal* probabilities. Notice that A and B here are not mutually exclusive events since it is possible for both to occur at the same time. Note also that A and B are not independent events since $P(A \cap B)$ $= .30 \neq P(A) \cdot P(B) = (.44) \times (.52) \cong .23$. For A and B to be independent it is necessary that

$$P(A|B) = \frac{P(A \cap B)}{P(B)} = P(A) .$$

This holds only when

$$\frac{n_{ab}}{n_{ab} + n_{\bar{a}b}} = \frac{(n_{ab} + n_{a\bar{b}})}{n} .$$

This means that in a table such as Figure 2–8 independence of A and B requires that the distribution of A and $\overline{A}$ within B must be the same as it is within $\overline{B}$, and as it is in the total without regard to whether or not B occurs. That is to say, the number of elements in the subset A which are also in B must be proportional to the number of elements in the universe set S which are in B.

2–8. BAYES' FORMULA

Approximately two hundred years ago a paper by the Reverend Thomas Bayes was published posthumously. In his paper Bayes developed a formula which is often referred to as Bayes' rule for probabilities of causes of events. The reasoning is as follows: Suppose that there are n mutually exclusive and collectively exhaustive events A_1, A_2, A_3, ... A_k, ..., A_n, called *prior* or *a priori* events, one of which is known to have occurred but it is not known which one. Suppose also that there is some other event B which has occurred and was preceded by or caused by one of the A_k. Which one is, of course, not known. Suppose we know the probabilities of the A_k, i.e., we know $P(A_1)$, $P(A_2)$, ...$P(A_k)$, ...$P(A_n)$. Suppose also that we know $P(B|A_1)$, $P(B|A_2)$, ...$P(B|A_k)$, ...$P(B|A_n)$. These are called the *likelihoods* of B, given A_k. What we want to know is $P(A_k|B)$ for all k. That is, we would like to know the probabilities that B was "caused" by each of the possible "causes." These are a *posteriori* or *posterior* probabilities. According to equation 2–16, for a given k,

$$P(A_k|B) = \frac{P(A_k \cap B)}{P(B)}.$$ (2-19)

We do not know $P(A_k \cap B)$ directly, but we do know, from Equation 2-17, that

$$P(A_k \cap B) = P(A_k) \cdot P(B|A_k).$$ (2-20)

Nor do we know $P(B)$. However, we know that $P(B)$ must be equal to the sum of the probabilities of all of the elements in B, regardless of which A_k they are in. Since by definition B must always appear in conjunction with one and only one A_k we can write

$$P(B) = P(B \cap A_1) + P(B \cap A_2) + \ldots + P(B \cap A_n).$$

This can be clarified further by reference to Figure 2-10, where $n = 4$. Here the subset B occurs in conjunction only with the subsets A_1, A_2, A_3 and A_4. B is the union of the intersections of $A_1 \cap B$, $A_2 \cap B$, $A_3 \cap B$, and $A_4 \cap B$.

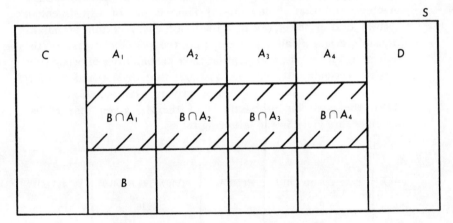

FIGURE 2-10. Intersection of B with A_1, A_2, ..., A_n

By applying Equation 2-20, we get

$$P(B) = P(A_1)P(B|A_1) + P(A_2)P(B|A_2) + \ldots + P(A_n)P(B|A_n)$$

$$= \sum_{k=1}^{n} P(A_k)P(B|A_k),$$ (2-21)

where $\sum_{k=1}^{n}$ means add all of the terms from the first through the nth.

Substituting Equations 2–20 and 2–21 into Equation 2–19 yields

$$P(A_k|B) = \frac{P(A_k)P(B|A_k)}{\displaystyle\sum_{k=1}^{n} P(A_k)P(B|A_k)}.$$

(2–22)

Equation 2–22 is known as *Bayes' formula* or *Bayes' rule*. It can be used to determine the probability that the event B was preceded by some particular A_k or each of the A_k in turn. The formula then may be useful in the search for the most likely cause of some particular event which is known to have occurred.

Example 2–14

Consider now a maintenance supervisor in a particular manufacturing plant. A certain machine is used for finishing ball bearings. Suppose that there are several points of adjustment on the machine and that if any one of them is out of adjustment, a certain kind of defect (event B) will occur with certain probabilities. More specifically, suppose that the possible causes of the defect are A_1, A_2, A_3, and A_4; that their probabilities of occurrence are, respectively, .01, .03, .02, and .02; that the likelihoods of B given A_1, A_2, A_3, and A_4 are, respectively, .45, .30, .25, and .50. Then the posterior probabilities of the A_k, given that B has occurred, are given in the following table:

$P(A_k)$	Prior Events (A_k)	$P(B|A_k)$	$P(A_k) \cdot P(B|A_k)$	$P(A_k|B)$
A_1	.01	.45	.0045	.16
A_2	.03	.30	.0090	.32
A_3	.02	.25	.0050	.17
A_4	.02	.50	.0100	.35
			.0285	1.00

Thus, $P(A_1|B) = .16$, $P(A_2|B) = .32$, $P(A_3|B) = .17$, and $P(A_4|B) = .35$. Our maintenance supervisor would, then, interpret this to mean that the most likely cause of the defect (event B) is adjustment A_4. The second most likely cause is adjustment A_2. Using this information, it is reasonable that he would check

these points of adjustment first and proceed from the most likely
to the least likely.

Example 2–15

Suppose it has been found that of people with less than a high
school education 65 per cent vote democratic, that of people who
are high school graduates with no college education 60 per cent
vote democratic; that of those with one to two years of college
51 per cent vote democratic; that of those with three or four
years of college 48 per cent vote democratic; but that of those
who have completed master's degrees and have no graduate work
beyond the master's, only 40 per cent vote democratic. Suppose
further that of those people who either have Ph.D. degrees or
have done some work on them, 75 per cent vote democratic.
Suppose also that the adult population in a particular town has
the following education distribution:

Event	Highest Education Level	Per Cent of Population
A_1	Less than high school	15
A_2	High school	37
A_3	One or two years college	23
A_4	Three or four years college	11
A_5	Master's degree	9
A_6	Ph.D. complete or in progress	5
	Total	100

Considering the percentages above as representing probabilities,
it is possible to determine the conditional probabilities of each of
the educational levels, given that a particular person has voted
democratic. That is, calling the occurrence of a democratic vote
the event B, we can apply Equation 2–22 to determine $P(A_k|B)$.
For example, given that a person has voted democratic, the probability that that person has a Ph.D. degree or is working on it is
given by

$$P(A_6|B) = \frac{(.05)(.75)}{(.65)(.15)+(.60)(.37)+(.51)(.23)+(.48)(.11)+(.40)(.09)+(.05)(.75)}$$

$$= \frac{.0375}{.0975 + .2220 + .1173 + .0528 + .0360 + .0375}$$

$$= \frac{.0375}{.5631} = .0666 .$$

Similarly, the probability that the individual has only a high school education, given that he voted democratic, is

$$P(A_2|B) = \frac{.2220}{.5631} = .3942$$

Before leaving Bayes' formula, a word of caution should be given. Equation 2–22 can be very useful, given knowledge of the probabilities of all of the prior events and the conditional likelihoods of B. However, in most practical business problems the prior probabilities are not known. Bayes himself recognized that this is usually the case in most real life problems. He suggested that, since we have no knowledge of these probabilities, they may just be treated as all being equal. This, however, is not a very satisfying solution to the problem and as a result Bayes' formula has not been used much over the past two hundred years or so since it was first introduced. In recent years, however, some statisticians (so called Bayesian statisticians) have contended that it is not necessary to assign equal probabilities to the prior events. Their argument generally is that the business man is in a position to draw on his experience and assign subjectively the probabilities of these events. He can then, it is argued, use these subjective prior probabilities of the A_k and the likelihoods of B given the A_k in Equation 2–22, to determine meaningful and useful posterior probabilities of the A_k given B.

Exercises

1. A box contains 95 good and 5 defective screws. If 5 of the screws are used, what is the probability that none of the 5 is defective?
   (Ans. $\frac{90}{95} \times \frac{89}{94} \times \frac{88}{93} \times \frac{87}{92} \times \frac{86}{91}$)
2. Two dice are thrown. Let A be the event that the sum of dots on the dice is odd and B the event that six dots appear on at least one of the dice. Find $P(A \cup B), P(A \cup \bar{B}), P(\bar{A} \cap B)$.
3. Suppose that from the digits (3, 4, 5, 6, 7, 8), first one is chosen at random and then a second is selected from the remaining five digits. What is the probability that an even digit will be selected (a) on the first selection, (b) on the second selection, (c) both times?
4. Prove that $P(A \cup B \cup C) = P(A) + P(B) + P(C) - P(A \cap B) - P(A \cap C) - P(B \cap C) + P(A \cap B \cap C)$.
5. Thirty cards are numbered consecutively from 1 through 30. Find

the probability that a number drawn at random (a) will end in 5, (b) is exactly divisible by 6, (c) will be odd.

(Ans. [a] $\frac{1}{10}$)

6. Find the probability that one card drawn at random from an ordinary deck of playing cards will be (a) a king, (b) a club, (c) the ace of spades, (d) a red card, (e) an honor card.

(Ans. [d] $\frac{1}{2}$)

7. From a bag containing four white, two red, and four black balls, one ball is drawn at random. Find the probability that it is (a) red, (b) not white.

(Ans. [b] $\frac{6}{10}$)

8. Suppose that 3 young lawyers (each aged 25) form a partnership. If the probability that a male aged 25 will live to be 65 years of age is .85, what is the probability that all 3 of them will live to this age? What is the probability that none of them will live to 65?

9. If three throws of a die are made in succession, find the probability that (a) the first two throws will result in sixes but the third one will not, (b) exactly two sixes will appear, (c) two consecutive sixes will appear, (d) the sum of dots for the three throws will be more than six.

(Ans. [d] $\frac{196}{216}$)

10. Four players are cutting for dealer in a game of contract bridge. Find the probability that all four will cut (a) an ace, (b) an honor card, (c) a card in the same suit.

11. Given $P(A) = .25$, $P(\bar{B}) = .60$, $P(A|B) = .30$, find $P(A \cup B)$, $P(A|\bar{B})$, $P(\bar{A} \cup \bar{B})$, $P(\overline{A \cup B})$, $P(A \cap B)$, $P(\bar{A} \cap \bar{B})$.

12. Given $P(A) = .60$, $P(B) = .40$, $P(A \cap B) = .24$, find $P(A|B)$, $P(A \cup B)$, $P(A|\bar{B})$, $P(B|A)$, $P(\bar{B})$. What is the relation between A and B?

13. Given $P(A) = .20$, $P(\bar{B}) = .45$, $P(A|B) = 0$, find $P(A|\bar{B})$, $P(\bar{A}|B)$, $P(A \cap B)$. What is the relation between A and B?

14. A player throws two dice, one red and the other green.
    (a) What is the probability that he will throw 7?
    (b) After the dice are thrown, an observer sees that the red die has turned up 3 but he cannot see the green die. What is the probability that a 7 has turned up, given that a 3 turned up on the red die?

(Ans. [a] $\frac{1}{6}$)

15. Prove that $P(A|B) = P(A)$ if A and B are independent.

16. A town has both a morning and an afternoon newspaper. Of the families in the town, 60 per cent buy the morning paper, 40 per cent buy the afternoon paper, and 15 per cent buy both. What per cent of the families buy neither paper?

17. If $P(X) = \frac{1}{2}$, $P(Y) = \frac{1}{3}$, and X and Y are independent events, what is the probability of either X or Y occurring? What is the probability that both X and Y will occur? What is the probability that neither X nor Y will occur?

(Ans. [both] $\frac{1}{6}$)

18. If $P(X) = \frac{1}{4}$, $P(Y) = \frac{2}{3}$, and X and Y are mutually exclusive, what is the probability that either X or Y will occur? What is the probability that both X and Y will occur? What is the probability that neither X nor Y will occur?

19. In a particular town 30 per cent of the families have incomes of $10,000 or more a year, and of these, two-thirds own houses worth $20,000 or more. Of those people with less than $10,000 a year, only 20 per cent own houses worth $20,000 or more. If you know that a particular house in this town is valued at $20,000 or more, what is the probability that its owner has at least a $10,000 income?

(Ans. .59)

20. From a closet containing five pairs of shoes we are to randomly select two shoes. What is the probability that we will select a matching pair?

(Ans. $\frac{1}{9}$)

21. In an experiment a man is given three cigarettes and is asked to smoke each and indicate whether it is brand A, brand B, or brand C. In his instructions he is told that there is one and only one of each of the brands among the three cigarettes given him so that each brand should be named once and only once. If he really can't tell the difference between the three brands, what are the possible outcomes of the experiment in terms of the number guessed correctly? What are the probabilities of each of these possible outcomes?

22. What is wrong with the following argument: "If two coins are tossed, there are three possible outcomes, two heads, one head and one tail, and two tails. Hence the probabilities of each of these outcomes is $\frac{1}{3}$."

23. If two dice are thrown, what are the various total numbers of dots that may turn up? What are the probabilities of each of these? What is the probability that the number of dots will total at least four?

24. In a role of five dice what is the probability of getting exactly four faces alike?

(Ans. $5^2/6^4$)

25. We have two bags. One contains four red and five black balls; the second contains six red and four black balls. In an experiment we will roll a die, and if at least five dots turn up we will select a ball from the first bag. If fewer than five dots turn up, we will select a ball from the second. What is the probability that we will select a red ball?

(Ans. $74/135$)

26. Given the information in Problem 25, suppose that a selection has been made and a red ball drawn. What is the probability that fewer than five dots turned up on the die?

27. Consider again the information in Problem 25. Suppose that we conducted the experiment as outlined in Problem 25 but that we then put the ball selected into the opposite bag and conducted the previous experiment again. What is the probability of a red ball on this draw? Given that a red ball is drawn on this selection, what is the probability that the second selection was preceded by the rolling of fewer than five dots?

28. Four men and their wives are to play two tables of bridge. If the men are paired with the women by drawing score cards, what is the probability that each man will draw his own wife for his partner?

29. Fifteen per cent of the employees of a particular company are graduates of business schools. Of these, 80 per cent are in administrative positions. Of those who have not been to business schools, 25 per cent are in administrative positions. What is the probability that an individual selected at random from the administrative staff is a business school graduate?

(Ans. .36)

30. Commercial radio stations are designated by call letters consisting of either three or four letters. If no restrictions were made as to which letter should be at the beginning or whether or not repetition is allowed, how many stations would be possible? If it is specified that all call "names" must begin with either a K or a W, but no restrictions are made as to repetition, how many stations could there be? How many stations are possible with "names" beginning with either K or W and allowing no repetition of letters?

31. Officials of a given state are considering the design of automobile license plates. The design under consideration is one with two

letters followed by four numerals. How many different licenses would be possible with this design? How many would be possible if all of those having four zeros are discounted (note that a blank space can be treated as a zero so that the license number AA1 would be interpreted as AA0001 as opposed to AA1000)? Since the letter "O" looks like a zero, it is decided that no license will be made containing an "O". How many licenses are possible in this case?

32. Many organizations are identified by their initials, such as **NASA**, **CIA**, **USSR**, **UNCL**, **CIO**, and **KKK**. How many three-letter initials are possible? How many four-letter initials are possible? How many four-letter initials are possible if no repetitions are allowed? How many four-letter initials are possible beginning with **U**, not allowing repetitions?

33. A committee of three people is to be selected from among seven people. If the first person selected is to be the chairman of the committee and the second person is to be the secretary, in how many ways can assignments to this committee be made? If the committee officers are to be selected on some basis other than order of selection, how many different committees can be selected?

$$\text{(Ans. 210; 35)}$$

34. How many different bridge hands can be selected from an ordinary deck of playing cards?

$$\left[\text{Ans.} \binom{52}{13} \right]$$

35. What is the probability of being dealt a five-card poker hand containing four black cards? Four aces?

$$\left[\text{Ans.} \frac{\binom{26}{4} \times \binom{26}{1}}{\binom{52}{5}}; \quad \frac{48}{\binom{52}{5}} \right]$$

36. What is the probability of being dealt a five-card poker hand containing one pair (two cards of the same kind)? Two pairs? Three of a kind? A full house (a pair and three of a kind)?

37. Six speakers are to speak at a political rally. In how many different orders can they appear on the program?

38. In how many different ways can four people seat themselves on a bench?

39. In how many different ways can four people seat themselves around a table if we are only interested in the way they are

seated in relation to each other and *not* how they are seated in relation to the table?

(Ans. 6)

40. Suppose that an automobile dealer has 20 cars but only has room for 5 in his show room. How many different groups of 5 could he select to put in the show room?

Selected References

Feller, W., *Introduction to Probability Theory and Its Application,* Vol. I, 2nd. ed., New York: John Wiley & Sons, Inc., 1957.

Freund, J. E., *Mathematical Statistics,* Ch. 2, Englewood Cliffs, N. J.: Prentice-Hall, Inc., 1962.

Goldberg, S., *Probability—An Introduction,* Englewood Cliffs, N. J.: Prentice-Hall, Inc., 1960.

Kemeny, J. G., A. Schleifer, J. L. Snell, and G. L. Thompson, *Finite Mathematics With Business Applications,* Ch. 4, Englewood Cliffs, N. J.: Prentice-Hall, Inc., 1962.

Meyer, P. L., *Introductory Probability and Statistical Applications,* Reading, Mass.: Addison-Wesley Publishing Co., Inc., 1965.

Schlaifer, R., *Probability and Statistics for Business Decisions,* New York: McGraw-Hill Book Company, Inc., 1959.

Uspensky, J. V., *Introduction to Mathematical Probability,* New York: McGraw-Hill Book Company, Inc., 1937.

Wadsworth, G. P., and J. G. Bryan, *Introduction to Probability and Random Variables,* New York: McGraw-Hill Book Company, Inc., 1960.

chapter three

Finite Stochastic Processes

3–1. OUTCOMES OF SEQUENCES OF EXPERIMENTS

In this chapter we will consider situations which involve sequences of experiments. We will be interested in the probabilities of obtaining specific sequences of outcomes of these experiments, as well as the overall outcomes of the sequences as a whole. Such sequences of trials whose outcomes are random in nature rather than deterministic are called *stochastic processes*. Most of the materials to be covered in the rest of this book involve stochastic processes of specific types. Here, we will be interested in stochastic processes in general. Let us visualize a sequence of experiments in which a trial is made. The outcome of this trial will determine which of several trials of a different type will be made, the outcome of which will determine the particular type of trial on the next step of the sequence, and so on. What we want to

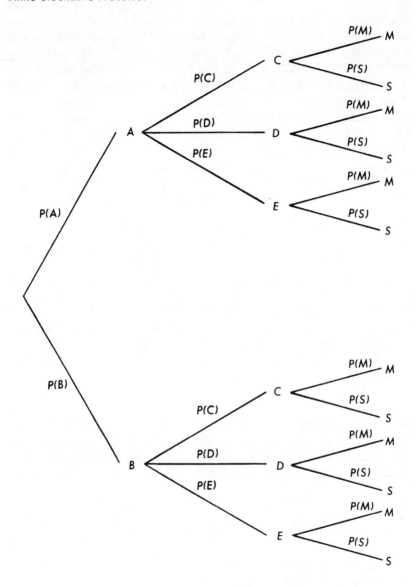

**FIGURE 3–1. Tree Diagram for Decision to
Study or Go to a Movie**

know is the probability that the whole sequence of trials will result
in a particular outcome.

More specifically, suppose that a ball is to be drawn from a bag
containing balls of two different types A and B with probabilities of

selection $P(A)$ and $P(B)$. Depending on the outcome of this selection, a ball is to be drawn from one or the other of two more bags (bag A and bag B) containing balls of three types C, D, and E, with probabilities $P(C|A)$, $P(D|A)$, and $P(E|A)$ if the selection is from bag A, or $P(C|B)$, $P(D|B)$, and $P(E|B)$ if the selection is from bag B. Then, depending on the outcome of this second selection, we will decide whether to spend the evening at the movie or studying (events M and S, respectively). We will make this final decision by drawing a ball from either bag C, D, or E (whichever type of ball was drawn on the preceding trial). If bag C is selected we will go to the movie with probability $P(M|C)$, or we will study with probability $P(S|C)$. Similarly, if bag D is selected the probabilities of movie and study respectively are $P(M|D)$ and $P(S|D)$; and if bag E is selected, these probabilities are $P(M|E)$ and $P(S|E)$. We want to know the probability that we will go to the movie or, conversely, that we will study. All of the possible outcomes of our experiment are indicated by the tree diagram in Figure 3–1. The probabilities of each possible outcome at each stage of the sequence are also indicated by the branches of the tree. The probability that we will follow any one of the twelve possible branches of the tree through the three sequences is given by the product of the probabilities attached to its branches. To illustrate, the probability that we will select a ball marked A first, then one marked C, and then one marked M is given by

$$P(A \cap C \cap M) = P(A)P(C|A)P(M|A \cap C) . \qquad (3\text{–}1)$$

What we really want to know, however, is the probability that, on the basis of this process, our decision will be to go to the movie. This probability will be given by the sum of the probabilities of all the possible ways of reaching the end branches of the tree labeled M. Thus,

$$P(M) = P(A \cap C \cap M) + P(A \cap D \cap M) + P(A \cap E \cap M) + P(B \cap C \cap M) + P(B \cap D \cap M) + P(B \cap E \cap M) .$$
$$(3\text{–}2)$$

Each of the terms in Equation 3–2 is, of course, determined according to Equation 3–1 above.

Example 3–1

Suppose that we have two bags. Bag 1 contains three red and two green balls, and Bag 2 contains four red and five green balls.

We will toss a coin and if a head turns up, we will select a ball from Bag 1. If a tail comes up, we will select a ball from Bag 2. What is the probability that we will select a green ball? At first glance it might be tempting to speculate that the probability of a green ball is .5 since there are altogether seven red and seven green balls involved. This, however, is not true. The situation described here can be depicted as a tree as in Figure 3–2. This

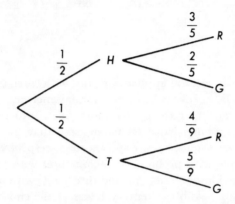

FIGURE 3–2. Tree Diagram to Determine the Probability of Selecting a Red or Green Marble

is a two-stage sequence. The probability of "head" on the coin is ½. Then the probability of a green ball, given that a "head" turned up, is ⅖. Hence, the probability of "head and green" is

$$P(H \cap G) = \left(\frac{1}{2}\right) \times \left(\frac{2}{5}\right) = \frac{1}{5}.$$

Similarly, the probability of "tail and green" is

$$P(T \cap G) = \left(\frac{1}{2}\right) \times \left(\frac{5}{9}\right) = \frac{5}{18}.$$

Finally, the probability of a green ball is

$$P(G) = P(H \cap G) + P(T \cap G)$$
$$= \left(\frac{1}{5}\right) + \left(\frac{5}{18}\right) = \frac{43}{90}.$$

Suppose now that in this example we were to select Bag 1 or Bag 2 from which to select a ball on the basis of the outcome of the toss of a die. Suppose that if a 5 or 6 turns up on the die we will make our selection from Bag 1; otherwise the selection will be made from Bag 2. The probability of selecting a green ball is

$$P(G) = \left(\frac{1}{3}\right) \times \left(\frac{2}{5}\right) + \left(\frac{2}{3}\right) \times \left(\frac{5}{9}\right)$$
$$= \frac{2}{15} + \frac{10}{27} = \frac{68}{135}.$$

Example 3–2

Consider an electric appliance dealer with three refrigerators on hand when he opens for business Monday morning. Let us assume that he is not to receive any more units into inventory until Thursday morning. Now, let us suppose that the possible daily demands over the next few days and their respective probabilities are zero units with probability .40, one unit with probability .30, two units with probability .20, and three units with probability .10. What are his possible inventory levels at the end of the working day Wednesday and what are their respective probabilities? We can analyze the problem by use of the tree diagram shown in Figure 3–3.

In Figure 3–3 the possible outcomes in terms of daily demands are given by the branches of the tree for each of the three days in question. The probabilities of each of these possible outcomes on Monday are indicated by the four branches of the tree to be .4, .3, .2, and .1. On Tuesday the number of units which can be sold will depend on the number sold the day before, as will the probabilities of each of these possibilities. For example, if two refrigerators are sold on Monday, the only two possible outcomes in terms of the number that will be sold are zero and one. The probability that none will be sold is .4 as indicated above. However, the probability that one will be sold is given by the sum of the probabilities that one, two, or three will be demanded. Hence, the probability that one will be sold is .6. The other probabilities in Figure 3–3 are determined similarly. Now, what we want to know are the possible levels of inventory at the end of business Wednesday, and their respective probabilities. Clearly, the possible levels of inventory are zero, one, two, and three units. Their

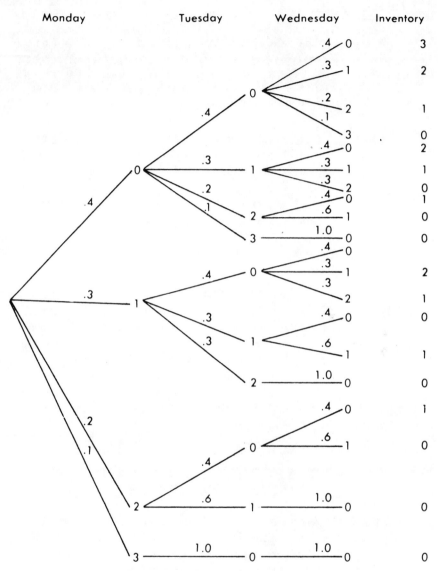

FIGURE 3–3. Tree Diagram for Inventory Problem

probabilities can be determined from the tree as the sum of the probabilities of all of the ways that they can result. Hence, the possible inventory levels and their probabilities are as follows:

Units in Inventory	Probability

0    $(.4)^2 \times (.1) + (.4) \times (.3)^2 + (.4) \times (.2) \times (.6)$
     $+ (.4) \times (.1) + (.3)^2 \times (.4) + (.3)^2 \times (.6)$
     $+ (.3)^2 + (.2) \times (.4) \times (.6) + (.2) \times (.6) + (.1)$
= .016 + .036 + .048 + .040 + .036 + .054 + .090
  + 0.48 + .120 + .100
= .588

1    $(.4)^2 \times (.2) + (.4) \times (.3)^2 + (.4) \times (.2) \times (.4)$
     $+ (.3) \times (.4) \times (.3) + (.3)^2 \times (.4) + (.2) \times (.4)^2$
= .032 + .036 + .032 + .036 + .036 + .032
= .204

2    $(.4)^2 \times (.3) + (.4) \times (.3) \times (.4) + (.3) \times (.4)^2$
= .048 + .048 + .048
= .144

3    $(.4)^3$
= .064 .

It should be noted that .588 + .204 + .144 + .064 = 1.0, which is simply to say that our appliance dealer is certain to have either none, one, two, or three of his refrigerators left after three days. The probability is very high, however, that he will not have more than one unit left. While this example is very highly simplified, it is somewhat suggestive of the way in which probability can be used in analyzing and controlling inventories of products for which demand is not certain but for which it is possible (usually by relative frequencies) to determine probabilities of various possible levels of demand.

3–2 INTRODUCTION TO FINITE MARKOV PROCESSES

A finite Markov process is a multi-stage stochastic or probabilistic process such that the conditional probability of being in any one of a finite number of states in stage $k + 1$ (given the past history of the process), depends only on the state the process is in in stage k for any integer k. More specifically, suppose that a sequence of experiments is conducted such that the possible outcomes on each experiment are $A_1, A_2, A_3, \ldots A_r$. Suppose further that the outcome on each experiment in the sequence is not independent of the outcomes on all previous experiments but is dependent only on the outcome of the immediately preceding experiment. Let us define p_{ij} to be the conditional probability of A_j on a given experiment, given that A_i occurred on the immediately preceding experiment, where i and j can take on all values $1, 2, \ldots r$. The outcomes A_i are referred to as *states* of the process. The individual experiments in the sequence are referred to as *stages* of the process. Thus, the kth experiment in the sequence is the kth stage of the process. The individual probabilities p_{ij} are the probabilities of making the *transition* from state i at the kth stage of the process to state j at the $(k + 1)$th stage. Hence, the p_{ij} are termed *transition probabilities*.

Transition probabilities can be exhibited in several ways. The most useful way is to arrange them in a square array as

$$P = \begin{bmatrix} p_{11} & p_{12} & p_{13} & \cdots & p_{1j} & \cdots & p_{1r} \\ p_{21} & p_{22} & p_{23} & \cdots & p_{2j} & \cdots & p_{2r} \\ \cdot & \cdot & \cdot & & \cdot & & \cdot \\ \cdot & \cdot & \cdot & & \cdot & & \cdot \\ \cdot & \cdot & \cdot & & \cdot & & \cdot \\ p_{i1} & p_{i2} & p_{i3} & \cdots & p_{ij} & \cdots & p_{ir} \\ \cdot & \cdot & \cdot & & \cdot & & \cdot \\ \cdot & \cdot & \cdot & & \cdot & & \cdot \\ \cdot & \cdot & \cdot & & \cdot & & \cdot \\ p_{r1} & p_{r2} & p_{r3} & \cdots & p_{rj} & \cdots & p_{rr} \end{bmatrix} \qquad (3\text{--}3)$$

Equation 3–3 is a special case of a *matrix* and is called a *transition matrix*. Matrices are fundamental to the study of Markov processes, and the transition matrix of a Markov process is its chief characteristic. An inadequate knowledge of the theory of matrices limits the extent to which the theory of Markov processes can be discussed. At this stage we can only hope to convey some conceptual understanding of the process and of its possible usefulness in practical problems.

Another way that transition probabilities may be demonstrated is by way of a transition diagram such as that shown in Figure 3–4. The arrows in Figure 3–4 indicate that if the process is in, say, state A_1 at stage k, in stage $k + 1$, it can either be in state A_1 with probability p_{11}; in state A_2 with probability p_{12}; or in state A_3 with probability p_{13}; but the probability of being in state A_4 is zero. The information in Figure 3–4, put in the form of a transition matrix, is

$$P = \begin{bmatrix} p_{11} & p_{12} & p_{13} & 0 \\ p_{21} & p_{22} & p_{23} & 0 \\ 0 & p_{32} & p_{33} & p_{34} \\ p_{41} & 0 & 0 & 0 \end{bmatrix}.$$

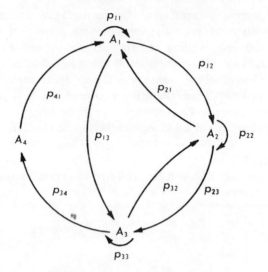

FIGURE 3–4. Transition Diagram

Notice that zero entries in the transition matrix mean that that particular transition is impossible; there is no arrow pointing from A_1 to A_4, or from A_3 to A_1, etc.

In applications of Markov *chains* we are usually interested in the probability that the process will be in state j after n stages, given that it started in state i. This probability is denoted by $p_{ij}^{(n)}$. Note that this is not the nth power of p_{ij}. The (n) in parentheses is a superscript which is used as a counter of the number of stages since beginning the process. Consider a Markov process with three possible states, A_1, A_2, and A_3. The probability of being in state A_1 after three stages of the process if the process started in A_1 is

$$
\begin{aligned}
p_{11}^{(3)} = {} & p_{11} \cdot (p_{11} \cdot p_{11} + p_{12} \cdot p_{21} + p_{13} \cdot p_{31}) + p_{12} \cdot (p_{21} \cdot p_{11} + p_{22} \\
& \cdot p_{21} + p_{23} \cdot p_{31}) + p_{13} \cdot (p_{31} \cdot p_{11} + p_{32} \cdot p_{21} + p_{33} \cdot p_{31}) \\
= {} & p_{11}p_{11}p_{11} + p_{11}p_{12}p_{21} + p_{11}p_{13}p_{31} + p_{12}p_{21}p_{11} + p_{12}p_{22}p_{21} \\
& + p_{12}p_{23}p_{31} + p_{13}p_{31}p_{11} + p_{13}p_{32}p_{21} + p_{13}p_{33}p_{31} .
\end{aligned}
$$

Here, $p_{11}p_{11}p_{11}$ represents the probability of staying in state one at all three stages; $p_{11}p_{12}p_{21}$ is the probability of staying in state one, then moving to state two, and then making the transition back to state one again. The other terms in the expression are interpreted similarly.

Similarly

$$
\begin{aligned}
p_{12}^{(3)} = {} & p_{11} \cdot (p_{11} \cdot p_{12} + p_{12} \cdot p_{22} + p_{13} \cdot p_{32}) + p_{12} \cdot (p_{21} \cdot p_{12} \\
& + p_{22} \cdot p_{22} + p_{23} \cdot p_{32}) + p_{13} \cdot (p_{31} \cdot p_{12} + p_{32} \cdot p_{22} \\
& + p_{33} \cdot p_{32}).
\end{aligned}
$$

By this same process we can compute all of the elements in the third stage three-state transition matrix

$$
P^{(3)} =
\begin{bmatrix}
p_{11}^{(3)} & p_{12}^{(3)} & p_{13}^{(3)} \\
p_{21}^{(3)} & p_{22}^{(3)} & p_{23}^{(3)} \\
p_{31}^{(3)} & p_{32}^{(3)} & p_{33}^{(3)}
\end{bmatrix} .
$$

Example 3–3

Suppose that we are interested in studying the mobility between size classes of manufacturing firms in the United States at ten-year intervals of time. Let us define three broad size classes, A_1, A_2, and A_3, where A_1 represents "large" firms in terms of number of employees, A_2 represents medium sized firms, and A_3 represents small firms. These are the three states of the process. Each stage of the process is a ten-year interval coinciding with census dates. Let us suppose that the transition matrix for the process is

$$
p^{(3)} =
\begin{bmatrix}
.7 & .3 & 0 \\
.2 & .6 & .2 \\
.1 & .3 & .6
\end{bmatrix} .
$$

According to this transition matrix, the probability that a large firm at one census date will also be large at the next is .7, the probability that it will be medium size is .3, and the probability that it will be small is 0. Similarly, the probability that a medium sized firm will move into the large category is .2, the probability that it will remain in the same category at the next stage of the process is .6, and the probability that it will drop down to the small category is .2. The last row of the matrix is interpreted similarly. It should be noted that the sum of the elements in each row of our transition matrix is 1. This is a characteristic which is necessary to all transition matrices since we have to make a transition to *some* state. In general terms, this is stated as

$$\sum_{j=1}^{r} p_{ji} = 1, \text{ where } i = 1, 2, \ldots, r. \qquad (3\text{--}4)$$

Suppose now that we want to know the probability that a firm in state A_1 will be in state A_1 after two stages of the process (i.e., twenty years later). This is

$$p_{11}^{(2)} = (.7) \times (.7) + (.3) \times (.2) + (0) \times (.1)$$
$$= .49 + .06$$
$$= .55.$$

The entire two-stage transition matrix is

$$P^{(2)} = \begin{bmatrix} .55 & .39 & .06 \\ .28 & .48 & .24 \\ .19 & .39 & .42 \end{bmatrix}.$$

Example 3–4

Consider a very important type of problem in which we are interested in determining the probabilities through time of alternative numbers of trucks waiting to be unloaded at a loading dock. (This is a special case of a general class of waiting line or queueing problems.) Suppose that we know from past experience the probabilities of alternative numbers of trucks per hour arriving to be unloaded as well as the probabilities of alternative numbers being unloaded and leaving the dock. With this information, and considering the stages of the process to be discrete intervals of one hour each, we can determine a transition matrix for the Markov process with the number of trucks waiting at the dock as the state variable. This can be done by considering, on the one hand, the alternative numbers of trucks that may arrive during an hour and their respective probabilities and, on the other hand, the numbers of trucks that leave the dock and their probabilities. The transition matrix may be constructed by constructing a tree diagram for each possible beginning number of trucks showing the numbers of trucks which may come and the numbers which may go. This is illustrated in Figure 3–5. Figure 3–5 assumes that the alternative numbers that may arrive and their probabilities, as

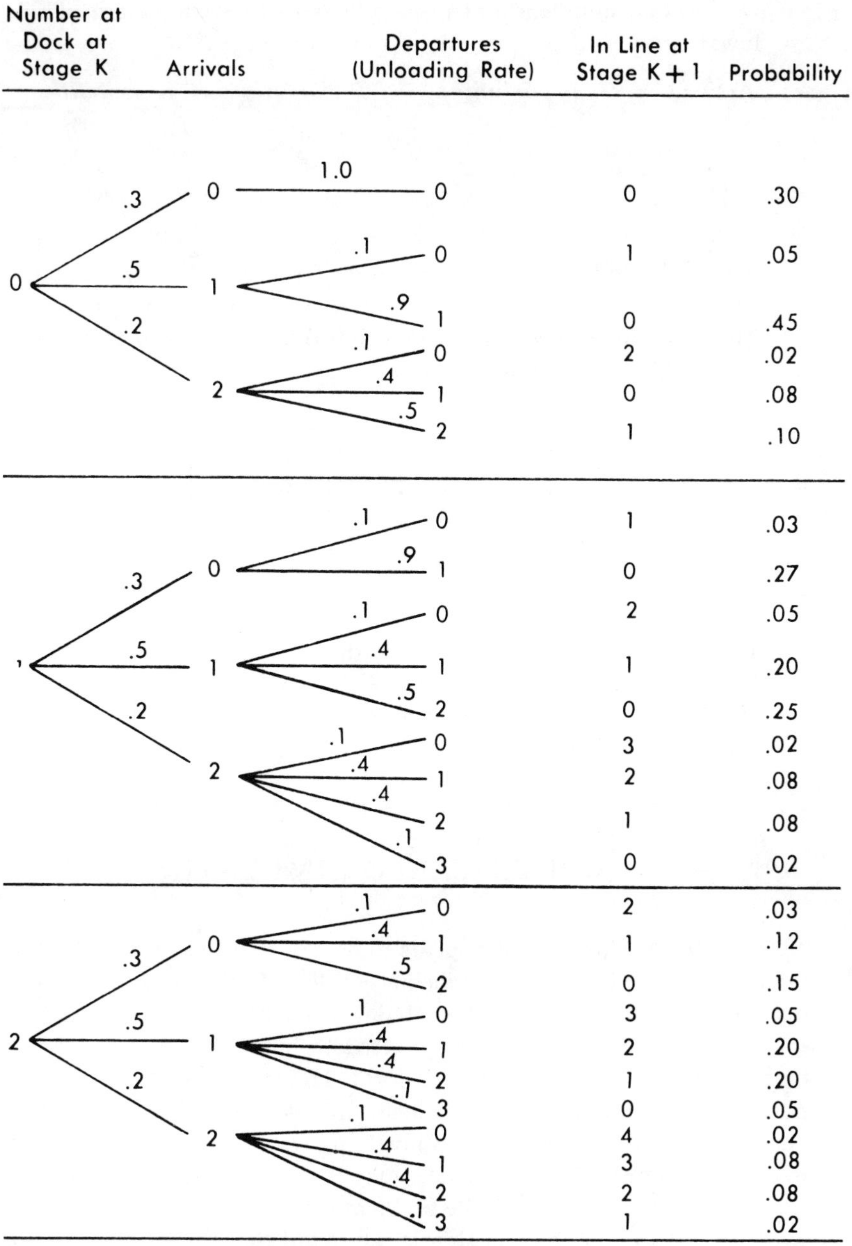

Number at Dock at Stage K	Arrivals	Departures (Unloading Rate)	In Line at Stage K+1	Probability
0	.3 → 0	1.0 → 0	0	.30
	.5 → 1	.1 → 0	1	.05
		.9 → 1	0	.45
	.2 → 2	.1 → 0	2	.02
		.4 → 1	0	.08
		.5 → 2	1	.10
	.3 → 0	.1 → 0	1	.03
		.9 → 1	0	.27
'	.5 → 1	.1 → 0	2	.05
		.4 → 1	1	.20
		.5 → 2	0	.25
	.2 → 2	.1 → 0	3	.02
		.4 → 1	2	.08
		.4 → 2	1	.08
		.1 → 3	0	.02
2	.3 → 0	.1 → 0	2	.03
		.4 → 1	1	.12
		.5 → 2	0	.15
	.5 → 1	.1 → 0	3	.05
		.4 → 1	2	.20
		.4 → 2	1	.20
		.1 → 3	0	.05
	.2 → 2	.1 → 0	4	.02
		.4 → 1	3	.08
		.4 → 2	2	.08
		.1 → 3	1	.02

FIGURE 3–5. Tree Diagram for Transition Probabilities in a Waiting Line Problem

well as the numbers and probabilities of departures, are as follows:

Arrivals	Probabilities	Departures	Probabilities
0	.3	0	.1
1	.5	1	.4
2	.2	2	.4
		3	.1

In Figure 3–5 we have determined the possible states of the system in stage $k + 1$ for three alternative possible states in k. The data in Figure 3–5 provide information for a partial transition matrix. The matrix would be

$$P = \begin{array}{c c} & \begin{array}{c c c c c} 0 & 1 & 2 & 3 & 4 & \cdots \end{array} \\ \begin{array}{c} 0 \\ 1 \\ 2 \end{array} & \left[\begin{array}{c c c c c} .85 & .13 & .02 & 0 & 0 & \cdots \\ .54 & .31 & .13 & .02 & 0 & \cdots \\ .20 & .34 & .31 & .13 & .02 & \cdots \\ \cdot & \cdot & \cdot & \cdot & \cdot \\ \cdot & \cdot & \cdot & \cdot & \cdot \\ \cdot & \cdot & \cdot & \cdot & \cdot \end{array} \right] \end{array} \; .$$

It should be clear to the student that this matrix could possibly have an infinite number of states. Unless the number possible is restricted to relatively few, this problem would be very difficult, if not impossible, to handle.

3–3. MONTE CARLO SIMULATION

Example 3–4 shows what appears to be a relatively simple and common problem situation, the queueing problem. If conditions surrounding the problem permit, Markov chain theory may be used to analyze the length of line that can be expected to build up, the time that a truck may expect to wait, and so forth. However, many problems in business involve very complex stochastic processes which cannot be analyzed directly. In many cases involving relatively simple processes, moreover, mathematical analysis may be cumbersome or difficult. As a case in point, although the problem set out in Example 3–4 is one which seems to be relatively simple, we found that the construction of the transition matrix for the system could turn into an almost impossible task.

By use of the so-called Monte Carlo simulation method it is possible to analyze in detail stochastic processes of any degree of complexity. The Monte Carlo method uses a random device to simulate a real-world stochastic process. We have used tree diagrams in many of the examples in this chapter to represent specific stochastic processes. To use the Monte Carlo method, we substitute for the tree diagram of a real stochastic process a simulated process having the same tree diagram. The method is carried out by use of a random device to generate artificial observations with the same probabilities as those in the real problem.

Example 3–5

Suppose that we are interested in analyzing the sequence of observations in a quality control problem involving the selection and testing of 10 photographic flash bulbs from a crate containing 100 bulbs, 3 of which are defective. What we are interested in specifically is the distribution of the number of defective bulbs in the sample and the probabilities of alternative numbers of bulbs. As we will see in later chapters, this problem can be handled fairly easily by direct mathematical analysis. However, at this point we want to analyze the problem experimentally. One possibility would be to actually select physically 10 bulbs from the crate and test them, then to get another crate of identical bulbs, select 10 from this crate and test them, and repeat the process a large number of times. In some of the samples there would be no defective bulbs, in some there would be 1, in some there would be 2, and in some there would be 3. We could then determine the relative frequencies in which each of these outcomes occurred and consider these to be the approximate probabilities of their occurrence. However, this would be a rather time-consuming and costly process. Instead of actually selecting bulbs and testing them, we could put 97 white and 3 red marbles of equal size into an urn, select 10 of the marbles and record the number of red ones selected. We could then replace those selected and, after mixing them thoroughly, select 10 more and record the number of red ones, and so on. This process can be continued for as many trials as is desired. If the number of trials is sufficiently large, the resulting relative frequencies will be approximately equal to the probabilities of selecting 0, 1, 2, or 3 defective bulbs.

Example 3–6

Consider again the problem in Example 3–4. Here there are several things of interest. However, we are primarily interested in the number of trucks that might be waiting to be unloaded at any given time and the probabilities of each of the alternatives. By the Monte Carlo method, this problem can be handled very easily. First we will label two urns A and D (representing arrivals and departures). Into urn A we will place 10 marbles of equal size and weight, 3 of which are red, 5 of which are green, and 2 of which are white. The selection of a red marble will signify that no trucks arrived in a given hour, a green will mean that 1 truck arrived, and a white will mean that 2 trucks arrived.

Similarly, into urn D we will place one yellow marble to represent zero departures, four orange marbles to represent one departure, four brown marbles to represent two departures, and one black marble to represent three departures. We are now in a position to carry out our sequence of experiments. We will begin by assuming that no trucks are waiting for service initially. Our sequence of experiments will proceed as follows: (1) select one marble each from urns A and D, observe their color, and interpret their color as indicated above. (2) Calculate $w_i = w_{i-1} + a_i - d_i$, where w_i denotes the number of trucks waiting at the end of hour i; w_{i-1} the number waiting at the end of hour $i-1$; a_i the number of arrivals during hour i; and d_i the number of departures during hour i. It should be obvious that w_i (the number waiting) can never be less than zero. Thus, if $d_i > w_{i-1} + a_i$, set $w_i = 0$. (3) Repeat (1) and (2) a large number of times (replacing the marbles selected each time before the next selection). Each repetition of the experiment represents an hour's experience. (4) Determine from the sequence of experiments the different numbers of trucks waiting and their relative frequencies. These will be their approximate probabilities of occurrence in the real problem. Moreover, from the sequence, $w_1, w_2, w_3, \ldots, w_i, w_{i+1}, \ldots w_n$, it would be possible to determine the relative frequencies of hour-to-hour changes from state to state, where the state is the number waiting for service at any given time. Hence, the simulated process can be used to estimate the transition matrix of the system.

In both of our examples we have simulated the stochastic process by selecting marbles from urns such that the numbers of various colored marbles in the urn were proportional to the probabilities characterizing the process being simulated. There are, of course, many other ways that this can be done. For example, we could use a spinner with equal divisions marked over the interval from 1 to 100. In many cases roulette wheels, dice, coins, or other similar devices may be used. In practice, however, simulations of complicated processes are usually carried out on electronic computers with the computer itself generating sequences of random numbers which conform to the probabilities of the alternative possible outcomes in the problem at hand. Although we will not develop this further here, these more complex simulations are conceptually the same as those already taken up.

It should be noted, however, that application of the Monte Carlo method is itself rather difficult in practice. Frequently, analytic methods such as those already covered are easier to use. Moreover, the Monte Carlo method does not yield exact answers, but only approximations.

Exercises

1. Draw transition diagrams for the Markov processes with transition probabilities as in the following matrices.

$$\begin{bmatrix} \dfrac{1}{2} & \dfrac{1}{2} \\[2mm] 1 & 0 \end{bmatrix} \qquad\qquad \begin{bmatrix} \dfrac{1}{3} & \dfrac{1}{2} & \dfrac{1}{6} \\[2mm] \dfrac{1}{2} & 0 & \dfrac{1}{2} \\[2mm] \dfrac{1}{3} & \dfrac{2}{3} & 0 \end{bmatrix}$$

$$\begin{bmatrix} .2 & .3 & .3 & .2 \\ .3 & .5 & .2 & 0 \\ .1 & .3 & .4 & .1 \\ 0 & .5 & 0 & .5 \end{bmatrix} \qquad \begin{bmatrix} .1 & 0 & .9 & 0 \\ 0 & 1 & 0 & 0 \\ .4 & .1 & .4 & .1 \\ 0 & .2 & .1 & .7 \end{bmatrix}$$

2. Find the matrix $P^{(2)}$ for the Markov chain determined by the following transition matrix.

$$P = \begin{bmatrix} .4 & .6 \\ .3 & .7 \end{bmatrix} \qquad \left(\text{Ans.} \quad \begin{bmatrix} .34 & .66 \\ .33 & .67 \end{bmatrix} \right)$$

3. Find the matrices $P^{(2)}$, $P^{(3)}$, $P^{(4)}$ for the Markov chain determined by the following transition matrix.

$$P = \begin{bmatrix} 1 & 0 & 0 \\ 0 & 1 & 0 \\ 0 & 0 & 1 \end{bmatrix}$$

4. Suppose that we have observed that when a shopper buys brand A canned peas on a given shopping trip, the probability is .8 that she will buy the same brand the next time she purchases peas and .2 that she will purchase brand B (assume that she will never purchase any other brand). On the other hand, if our shopper purchases brand B on a given trip, the probability that she will buy B again the next time is .6 and the probability that she will buy brand A is .4. (a) Set up the transition matrix for this shopper. (b) Calculate $P^{(2)}$. (c) If she begins the process by tossing a die and buying brand A if either 5 or 6 dots turn up and brand B otherwise, what is the probability that she will buy brand A on her third purchase?

5. Markov chains have been used on a number of occasions to study the social mobility of people from generation to generation. Suppose that we use occupational groupings as a measure of social status and that we group occupations into three major classes, professional and managerial, skilled, and unskilled. Suppose that we have observed that 85 per cent of the sons of men in the professional and managerial class are also in this class, 8 per cent are skilled, and 3 per cent are unskilled. Forty per cent of the sons of skilled workers are in the professional and managerial class, 40 per cent are skilled, and 20 per cent are unskilled. Finally, suppose that of sons of unskilled workers 20 per cent become professional or managerial personnel, 45 per cent are skilled, and 35 per cent are unskilled. (a) Set up the transition matrix. (b) Calculate $P^{(2)}$. (c) From (b), given that a man is an unskilled worker, what is the probability that his grandson will be in the professional and managerial class?

6. A box of screws contains 97 good screws and 3 defective ones. Suppose that we select at random 3 screws consecutively from the box without replacement. Draw a tree depicting the possible outcomes and their probabilities for this process.

7. Suppose that you are trying to decide whether to stay home and study tonight or to go to see the movie that you have been wanting to see. Suppose further that the probability that you will have a math test tomorrow is .3; that if you study tonight the probability that you will pass the test if it is given is .9; but if you do not study, the probability of pass is only .6. Of course, if no test is given, there is no problem. Assume that you decide on whether to go to the movie or to study by tossing a coin (head, to the movie; tail, study). Draw a tree diagram of

the problem and determine the probability of passing the test, given that there is a test.

8. Toss 4 coins 100 times, recording each time the number of heads on each toss. Using these observations, construct a relative frequency distribution of the number of heads per toss.

9. A large automobile dealer is studying the behavior of his inventory of a particularly popular car. He has observed that the daily demand for this model has never been for more than 4 cars and tends to behave in the same way as the number of heads on the toss of 4 coins. Assume that when we start observation of the process there are 12 cars in inventory and that the policy is to reorder 12 cars when the inventory level drops to 6 and that the shipment is always received at the close of the third day after the order is placed. Units demanded when not available are back-ordered and the demand is filled on receipt of the shipment. Simulate 30 days' operation of the system.

Selected References

Feller, W., *Introduction to Probability Theory and Its Applications,* Vol. I, 2nd. ed., New York: John Wiley & Sons, Inc., 1957.

Kemeny, J. G., A. Schleifer, J. L. Snell, and G. L. Thompson, *Finite Mathematics with Business Applications,* Englewood Cliffs, N. J.: Prentice-Hall, Inc., 1962.

Kemeny, J. G., and J. L. Snell, *Finite Markov Chains,* Princeton, N. J.: D. Van Nostrand Co., Inc., 1962.

Parzen, E., *Stochastic Processes,* San Francisco: Holden-Day, Inc., 1962.

part 2

Distributions of
Discrete Random
Variables

chapter four

Discrete Random Variables and Expectation

4–1. BASIC CONCEPTS

Suppose that we conduct an experiment such that its outcomes can be viewed as the number of occurrences of some event. For example, suppose that we toss five coins and define the outcomes of the toss as the number of heads that occur. Or suppose that we toss two dice and define the outcomes as the sum of dots on the two dice. In the case of the five coins, the outcomes would be either 0, 1, 2, 3, 4, or 5 heads. In the case of the two dice the outcomes would be either 2, 3, 4, . . ., 11, 12 dots. Any given toss of the five coins will result in either 0, 1, 2, 3, 4, or 5 heads. Similarly any given toss of the two dice will result in either 2, 3, 4, . . ., 12 dots. We have no way of knowing in advance how many heads will occur. Nor do we have any way of knowing how many dots will occur. We can, however, determine the probabilities attached to each of the possibilities.

Let us now define the quantity X to be a *random variable* which can take on any one of the mutually exclusive *values* x over the range of X. In the present case the specific values x are integer values and we define X to be a *discrete random variable*. (In this book only discrete random variables will be treated.) In addition to the number of heads on a given number of coins or the number of dots on a given number of dice, our random variable X may represent any number of different things such as the number of defective screws in a box, the number of people voting favorably in a bond election, or the number of telephone calls coming into a particular telephone exchange within a given period of time.

A random variable X is defined such that for each value x we can determine a probability $f(x)$ that X takes on that particular value. That is, we define the probability

$$P(X = x) = f(x) .$$

Here $f(x)$ is the *probability density function* (sometimes referred to as the *probability function* or the *density function*) of X.

Example 4–1

Suppose that our random variable is the number of heads on the toss of three coins. Then, the possible values of the X and their probabilities are

$$P(X = 0) = f(0) = \frac{1}{8}$$

$$P(X = 1) = f(1) = \frac{3}{8}$$

$$P(X = 2) = f(2) = \frac{3}{8}$$

$$P(X = 3) = f(3) = \frac{1}{8} .$$

This is an example of a special and very important type of probability distribution, known as the binomial probability distribution. The binomial distribution will be discussed in detail in Chapter 6.

Example 4–2

Suppose that on the basis of relative frequencies the daily demand (number of units demanded) for a particular perishable commodity at a small town grocery store has the following distribution

$$P(X = 0) = f(0) = .3679$$

$$P(X = 1) = f(1) = .3679$$

$$P(X = 2) = f(2) = .1839$$

$$P(X = 3) = f(3) = .0613$$

$$P(X = 4) = f(4) = .0153$$

$$P(X = 5) = f(5) = .0037[1]$$

This is known as a Poisson distribution with its parameter equal to one. Poisson distributions will be discussed in Chapter 7.

For every x, there is a corresponding $f(x)$ which is the probability of that particular value of X. It should be noted again that the individual values of X are mutually exclusive so that the exhaustive sum of the probabilities of x over the range of X is equal to 1. Namely,

$$\sum_x f(x) = 1.$$

We should also define the *distribution function* of X. The distribution function $F(x)$ is defined as

$$P(X \le x) = F(x).$$

That is to say, the distribution function is the cumulative probability function of the X from the smallest up to some specific value of x. In the daily demand example above, $F(1) = .7358$. Similarly, in the coin example above, $F(2) = \frac{7}{8}$. We will have ample opportunity to make use of distribution functions later, but in the meantime we need to examine certain other important characteristics and uses of density functions of random variables.

---

[1]Actually this is equal to $P(X \ge 5)$ rather than $P(X = 5)$. However, $P(X > 5)$ by this type of distribution is so small that we will ignore this problem here.

4–2. MATHEMATICAL EXPECTATION

The *mathematical expectation* or *expectation*, or *expected value* (these terms are used interchangeably) of a random variable is defined as follows:

$$E(X) = \sum_x x \cdot f(x) . \qquad\qquad (4-1)$$

In words, the expected value of a random variable is the sum of the products of all possible values of the random variable and their respective probabilities.

Example 4–3

In the case of the toss of three coins in Example 4–1, the expected number of heads is given in the following table:

x	$f(x)$	$xf(x)$
0	$\dfrac{1}{8}$	0
1	$\dfrac{3}{8}$	$\dfrac{3}{8}$
2	$\dfrac{3}{8}$	$\dfrac{6}{8}$
3	$\dfrac{1}{8}$	$\dfrac{3}{8}$

$$E(X) = \frac{12}{8} = 1.5$$

Hence, the expected number of heads on the toss of three coins is 1.5. This does not mean that we actually "expect" to get 1.5 heads on any given toss of three coins. We know that this is impossible; we cannot get half a head on the toss of an ordinary coin.

What the expected value in Example 4-1 means is that if we were to toss three coins a very large number of times, assuming independent outcomes, we would expect *on the average* to get 1.5 heads. It can be shown mathematically that as the number of tosses becomes large, the observed average number of heads that will occur on the toss of three coins gets close to 1.5.

The expected value of a random variable, then, is the average value of that variable over a very large number of trials. This expected value may actually be impossible on any given trial.

Example 4–4

Consider now the distribution of daily demand in Example 4–2, and assume that the maximum demand is for five units. Then the expected or average daily demand over a long period of time is given by the following table:

x	f(x)	xf(x)
0	.3679	.0000
1	.3679	.3679
2	.1839	.3678
3	.0613	.1839
4	.0153	.0612
5	.0037	.0185

$$E(X) \;=\; .9993 \;\cong\; 1.0000$$

In the above table, if we had not assumed that the maximum demand was five units but had considered the possibility of six, seven, eight, etc. units demanded, $E(X)$ would have been exactly equal to one. As was indicated earlier, the distribution of daily demand in this case is a Poisson distribution with the parameter equal to one. Such distributions will be taken up in detail in Chapter 7.

Example 4–5

As another example, suppose that we toss a pair of dice a large number of times. If X is the number of dots that turn up on the two dice and $f(x)$ is the probability that $X = x$, we can determine the expected number of dots as follows:

x	$f(x)$	$xf(x)$
2	$\dfrac{1}{36}$	$\dfrac{2}{36}$
3	$\dfrac{2}{36}$	$\dfrac{6}{36}$
4	$\dfrac{3}{36}$	$\dfrac{12}{36}$
5	$\dfrac{4}{36}$	$\dfrac{20}{36}$
6	$\dfrac{5}{36}$	$\dfrac{30}{36}$
7	$\dfrac{6}{36}$	$\dfrac{42}{36}$
8	$\dfrac{5}{36}$	$\dfrac{40}{36}$
9	$\dfrac{4}{36}$	$\dfrac{36}{36}$
10	$\dfrac{3}{36}$	$\dfrac{30}{36}$
11	$\dfrac{2}{36}$	$\dfrac{22}{36}$
12	$\dfrac{1}{36}$	$\dfrac{12}{36}$

$$E(X) = \frac{252}{36} = 7$$

Hence, the expected number of dots on a toss of a pair of dice is seven. In other words, on the average, we would expect a seven to show up. Moreover, this is the most likely number of dots too, since $f(7) = \frac{6}{36}$, which is the largest value in the $f(x)$ column.

4–3. EXPECTED VALUE AND FAIR GAMES

Example 4–6

Suppose that in our Example 4-1 above of the toss of three coins, we were to ask a friend to join us in a game in which we will toss the three coins. We will pay him $.05 if we get fewer than three heads, and he will pay us $.15 if we get three heads. What is the value of this game to us? To answer this question, let us define a new random variable (call it M) to represent our monetary *payoff* depending on the outcome of the game. If m_1 is the payoff attached to the occurrence of fewer than three heads, then m_1 is equal to $-.05$ and m_2 (the payoff attached to the occurrence of three heads) is equal to $+.15$. The probability of m_1 $[P(M = m_1) = f(m_1)]$ is the sum of the probabilities of zero, one, and two heads; the probability of m_2 is the probability of getting three heads. Namely,

$$P(M = m_1) = f(m_1) = f(x_1) + f(x_2) + f(x_3) = \frac{1}{8} + \frac{3}{8} + \frac{38}{8} = \frac{7}{8}$$

and

$$P(M = m_2) = f(m_2) = f(x_4) = \frac{1}{8}.$$

Therefore, the expected payoff (the expected value of the game to us) is

$$E(M) = -.05\left(\frac{7}{8}\right) + .15\left(\frac{1}{8}\right) = -\frac{.35}{8} + \frac{.15}{8} = -\frac{.20}{8} = -\$.025 .$$

That is, if we were to play this game over and over a large number of times, we would expect on the average to lose two and one-half cents each toss. Conversely, our friend could expect to win the same amount on each toss. Thus, if our friend were to give us $.025 each time before a toss is made, the expected value of the game to us and to our friend would be zero. We call such a game a *fair game*. It is *fair* in the sense that it is not weighted in favor of either of us. Hence, a fair game is a game with zero expectation.

Example 4–7

Suppose now that our friend suggests that we play a game in which we will draw a card from a well shuffled deck of ordinary playing cards. If we draw an ace, he will pay us $5.00; if we draw a king or queen, he will pay us $2.50; if we draw a jack, ten, or nine, he will pay us $.75. Otherwise, we are to pay him $1.00. Is the game fair? In order to determine the value of the game, let us set up a table as follows:

Event	Payoff m	Probability $f(m)$	$mf(m)$
Ace	$ 5.00	$\dfrac{1}{13}$	$\dfrac{5}{13}$
King or queen	2.50	$\dfrac{2}{13}$	$\dfrac{5}{13}$
Jack, ten, nine	.75	$\dfrac{3}{13}$	$\dfrac{2.25}{13}$
Less than nine	-1.00	$\dfrac{7}{13}$	$\dfrac{-7}{13}$

$$E(M) = \frac{5.25}{13} \cong .404$$

The value of the game to us is approximately 40.4 cents. Thus it is weighted in our favor and is not a fair game.

Since, in this example, the game is "worth" 40.4 cents to us, we should be willing to pay him anything up to this amount to permit us to play the game. At the same time, he should be willing to accept anything more than this amount for permitting us to play. If we pay less than 40.4 cents per play of the game, we could expect in the long run to come out ahead and our friend could expect to be the loser. If we paid more than this amount, our friend would expect to come out ahead and we would be the losers.

We have said that we should be willing to pay up to the value of the game (but no more) to play the game, because if we paid more than the value of the game (or accepted less) we could lose in the long run. It would not be rational to voluntarily accept a loss.

However, it is obvious that many people do voluntarily accept losses by gambling in casinos where the expected values of the games to them are negative. If the values of the games to the "customers" in casinos were not negative, they could not long remain in business. Perhaps, in this case, people are willing to pay for the enjoyment of playing and for the possibility of striking it rich.

An interesting and very famous example of the difficulty which may arise in connection with "fair" games is the so-called *St. Petersburg Paradox* which was first discussed in the 18th century by the mathematician Daniel Bernoulli. The game is one such that a coin is tossed until the first head turns up. If a head turns up on the first toss the payoff is \$2. If it turns up on the second toss the payoff is \$$2^2$ = \$4. In general, if the first head turns up on the ith toss, the payoff is \$$2^i$. However, the probability that the first head will turn up on the toss is $\frac{1}{2}^i$. Since there is no limit to the number of possible tosses, the expected value of the game is

$$E(M) = \sum_{i=1}^{\infty} 2^i \cdot \left(\frac{1}{2^i}\right) = \infty .$$

Thus, it might be argued that to make the game "fair" one should be willing to pay an infinite amount to play the game. Certainly no one would be willing to do this. In the first place, no one has completely unlimited resources with which to enter the game. In the second place the small probability of an unlimited gain certainly cannot outweigh, in the mind of the ordinary person, the rather large probability of an unlimited loss if he did manage to put up the money to play.

This brings up notions of "utility" which will only be mentioned here. That is to say, a given amount of money potentially lost to a particular individual might be viewed by him as being worth more to him (a greater *utility* lost) than the same amount potentially gained. For another individual (or the same one under a different set of circumstances) a given potential dollar gain might have greater utility than the same potential dollar loss. The exact relation between the utilities of given potential gains or losses depends upon the circumstances of the individual at any given time. A person who, for example, faces a possible jail sentence if he doesn't raise a large sum of money immediately might be willing to risk almost anything in an effort to avoid going to jail, even though the expected monetary value of the venture might be quite small. All of this is simply to say that the expected *utility* of the game is really the deciding factor rather than the expected monetary value. Utilities in this sense are purely subjective and simply represent an individual's evaluation of the "worth" to him of a potential monetary gain relative to a loss.

4–4. THE MEAN AND VARIANCE OF A RANDOM VARIABLE

We have already said that the expected value of a random variable can be thought of as the average value of the variable over a very long series of trials. Another term used for this same concept is the *mean*. The mean of a random variable is usually denoted by the lower case Greek letter Mu (μ). Thus the mean of a random variable is

$$\mu = \sum_{i=1}^{n} x_i f(x_i) = E(X),$$

(4–2)

where X takes on values $x_1, x_2, \ldots, x_n$, with probabilities $f(x_1)$, $f(x_2)$, $\ldots, f(x_n)$. This is the notation which is used in the study of statistics as well as in the study of certain special probability distributions.

In our example of the number of heads on the toss of three coins, $\mu = 1.5$. Similarly, in the example of the number of dots on a pair of dice $\mu = 7$. The mean notation, however, is not usually used in connection with the expected value of a game, although there is no reason why it could not be done.

In our examples so far we have been concerned with the average, or mean, or expected value of our random variable. We recognized that, although we referred to this as the "expected" value, we do not "expect" that it will always occur. Indeed, we even stated that in many cases the "expected" value is known to be impossible; 1.5 heads, for example. The notion of an expected value as we have used it refers simply to an average occurrence over a large number of trials. Since we recognize that more often than not some value other than the expected value will occur, it would be helpful to have a measure of the expected amount that our random variable will differ from its mean or expected value. We might go about trying to construct such a measure by subtracting the mean from each value of X and then calculating the expected value of these differences. This would be done as follows:

$$E(X - \mu) = \sum_{i=1}^{n} (x_i - \mu) f(x_i) .$$

However,

$$\sum_{i=1}^{n} (x_i - \mu) f(x_i) = \sum_{i=1}^{n} [x_i f(x_i) - \mu f(x_i)]$$

$$= \sum_{i=1}^{n} x_i f(x_i) - \mu \sum_{i=1}^{n} f(x_i) .$$

And

$$\sum_{i=1}^{n} x_i f(x_i) = \mu \text{ and } \sum_{i=1}^{n} f(x_i) = 1 .$$

So

$$E(X - \mu) = \mu - \mu = 0 .$$

The expected value of deviations of values of X from their mean is always equal to zero. Therefore, we need another measure of the spread of the values of X from the mean. The reason that $E(X - \mu) = 0$ is that some of the individual differences are positive and some are negative. Moreover, the expected value of the positive deviations is exactly equal to the expected value of the negative ones.

One way we can get around this problem is to *square* the individual deviations and then determine the expected value of their squares. The expected value of the squared deviations from μ is called the *variance* of X and is defined as

$$\sigma^2 = \sum_{i=1}^{n} (x_i - \mu)^2 f(x_i) = E(X - \mu)^2 . \qquad (4\text{--}3)$$

The variance then is the expected value of the squared difference between the individual values of the random variable and the mean. Equation 4-3 can be made more operational by squaring the parentheses and simplifying as

$$\sigma^2 = \sum_{i=1}^{n} (x_i - \mu)^2 \cdot f(x_i) = \sum_{i=1}^{n} (x_i^2 - 2\mu \cdot x_i + \mu^2) \cdot f(x_i)$$

$$= \sum_{i=1}^{n} x_i^2 \cdot f(x_i) - 2\mu \cdot \sum_{i=1}^{n} x_i \cdot f(x_i) + \mu^2 \cdot \sum_{i=1}^{n} f(x_i) .$$

But

$$\sum_{i=1}^{n} x_i \cdot f(x_i) = \mu, \text{ and } \sum_{i=1}^{n} f(x_i) = 1 .$$

So,

$$\sigma^2 = \sum_{i=1}^{n} x_i^2 f(x_i) - \mu^2 .$$

Or stated somewhat more succinctly,

$$\sigma^2 = E(X^2) - [E(X)]^2. \qquad (4\text{--}4)$$

The square root of the variance (σ) is called the *standard deviation*. This is of particular importance because it measures the deviations of the variable from its expected value in the same units of measure as the variable itself, whereas the variance measures squared deviations. Hence, the standard deviation of a distribution is defined as

$$\sigma = \sqrt{E(X^2) - [E(X)]^2}. \qquad (4\text{--}5)$$

Example 4–8

In our toss of three coins earlier we found that the expected number of heads, or the mean, was $\mu = 1.5$. We can determine the variance and the standard deviation of the number of heads as follows:

x	$f(x)$	$xf(x)$	$x^2f(x)$
0	$\dfrac{1}{8}$	0	0
1	$\dfrac{3}{8}$	$\dfrac{3}{8}$	$\dfrac{3}{8}$
2	$\dfrac{3}{8}$	$\dfrac{6}{8}$	$\dfrac{12}{8}$
3	$\dfrac{1}{8}$	$\dfrac{3}{8}$	$\dfrac{9}{8}$

$$E(X) = \mu = 1.5 \qquad E(X^2) = \frac{24}{8} = 3$$

Thus,

$$\sigma^2 = 3 - (1.5)^2 = .75, \text{ and}$$
$$\sigma = .866.$$

That is to say, on the average 1.5 heads will turn up on the toss of three coins, and on the average the number of heads turning up will differ from 1.5 by about .866.[2] As we will see shortly, the standard deviation of a distribution may be used to tell us something about the probability of occurrence of certain values of x when we might not be able to determine these probabilities directly.

---

[2]This is a peculiar sort of "average." Actually, it is the square root of the average amount of squared deviation.

Example 4–9

Let us look again at the average daily demand problem. We found from the distribution of daily demands for our perishable product that the average daily demand was .9994, or approximately 1. We are now in a position to measure the average amount of deviation of daily demands from this mean. Consider the following table:

x	f(x)	xf(x)	$x^2f(x)$
0	.3679	.0000	.0000
1	.3679	.3679	.3679
2	.1839	.3678	.7356
3	.0613	.1839	.5517
4	.0153	.0612	.2448
5	.0037	.0185	.0925

$$E(X) = \mu = .9994 \quad E(X^2) = 1.9925$$

Thus,

$$\sigma^2 = 1.9925 - (.9994)^2 = 1.9925 - .9988 = .9937 \cong 1,$$

$$\sigma = .9969 \cong 1 .$$

In this case we see that the average daily demand for the product is approximately one unit and that the standard deviation (or average amount of variation around the mean) is also approximately one. As already indicated, this is a Poisson distribution with its parameter equal to one. As will be shown in Chapter 7, it is a characteristic of the Poisson distribution that the mean and variance are equal.

Example 4–10

Now let us consider again the problem of the dice. We found before that the expected value or mean number of dots is 7. From a table similar to those already used, we can determine the variance of the number of dots. It will be left to the reader to verify that $\sigma^2 = 5.83$. Hence, $\sigma \cong 2.41$.

4–5. THE THEOREM OF TCHEBYSHEFF

Consider the distribution of a random variable X which has expected value μ and variance σ^2. Suppose that we mark off boundaries on the scale of possible values of X as follows:

Now, the variance of X is defined as

$$\sigma^2 = \sum_i (x_i - \mu)^2 \cdot f(x_i),$$

where i ranges over all elements in the universe. Let us now append the subscript j to all elements with values of X such that

$$\mu - \alpha\sigma \leq x_j \leq \mu + \alpha\sigma \,.$$

Similarly, let us append the subscript k to all of the elements with values of X such that either $x_k < \mu - \alpha\sigma$ or $x_k > \mu - \alpha\sigma$.

Then we can divide the sum above into two parts as

$$\sigma^2 = \sum_j (x_j - \mu)^2 \cdot f(x_j) + \sum_k (x_k - \mu)^2 \cdot f(x_k).$$

The first sum here includes all of the elements with values within the boundaries laid off above, and the second sum includes the elements outside the boundaries. Since all of the terms in both sums must be positive, we see that

$$\sigma^2 \geq \sum_k (x_k - \mu)^2 \cdot f(x_k)$$

Now, since each of the $(x_k - \mu)^2 > (\alpha\sigma)^2$, we can replace each $(x_k - \mu)^2$ in the sum by its lower bound $(\alpha\sigma)^2$. Hence,

$$\sigma^2 > \sum_k (\alpha\sigma)^2 \cdot f(x_k).$$

But since both α and σ are constant,

$$\sigma^2 > (\alpha\sigma)^2 \sum_k f(x_k).$$

Or,

$$\sum_k f(x_k) < \frac{\sigma^2}{(\alpha\sigma)^2} = \frac{1}{\alpha^2}.$$

Now,

$$\sum_k f(x_k) = P(|X - \mu| > \alpha\sigma),$$

where $|X - \mu|$ means the difference between a value of X selected at random and μ, ignoring the sign. Thus

$$P(|X - \mu| > \alpha\sigma) < \frac{1}{\alpha^2}. \qquad (4\text{--}6)$$

In Equation 4–6 we have shown what is known as Tchebysheff's inequality, or Tchebysheff's theorem. In words, in Equation 4–6, we are saying that the probability of occurrence of a value of X which differs from its mean by more than $\alpha\sigma$ is less than $1/\alpha^2$. For example, regardless of the nature of our probability distribution, the probability of occurrence of the value of X which differs from its mean by more than two standard deviations is not more than $\frac{1}{4}$.

Example 4–11

In our earlier example (4–9) of daily demand we can say, by Equation 4–6, that the probability that demand on any given day will differ from one unit by more than two units is not more than $\frac{1}{4}$. If we look at the table on page 74, we see that this probability is in fact only .0190, which is substantially less than $\frac{1}{4}$. In the case of the dice, by Tchebysheff's theorem, the probability of getting more than 11.82 or less than 2.18 dots on a pair of dice is not more than $\frac{1}{4}$. From the table on page 67 we see that this probability is actually only $\frac{1}{18}$. Hence, in Equation 4–6 rough outside limits are set on the probability that a random variable will differ from its mean by more than α standard deviation units.

Example 4–12

Not all probability distributions are so well behaved as those in the earlier examples. Consider, for example, the distribution in the following table:

x	$f(x)$	$x f(x)$	$x^2 f(x)$
0	.24	.0000	.0000
1	.18	.1800	.1800
2	.08	.1600	.3200
3	.08	.2400	.7200
4	.18	.7200	2.8800
5	.24	1.2000	61.0000

$$E(X) = \mu = 2.5 \quad E(X^2) = 10.10$$

In this case $\mu = 3.5$ and the variance is

$$\sigma^2 = 10.10 - (2.5)^2 = 3.85 .$$

So,

$$\sigma^2 \cong 1.96 .$$

Then, by the use of Equation 4–6, the probability of occurrence of a value of X less than -1.42 or greater than 6.42 is not more than $\frac{1}{4}$. In the case of our distribution above, the probability of a value of X greater than 6.42 is zero, and the probability of a value of X less than -1.42 is 0. Hence, in this case the probability of a value of X outside the range of $\mu \pm 2\sigma$ is actually 0 as compared to the maximum possible probability, by Tchebysheff's theorem, of .25. This is an extreme example.

For most distributions which are ordinarily encountered, the actual probability is substantially less than given in Equation 4–6. The inequality can be of considerable usefulness in giving some notions of probabilities within specified ranges of values for distributions of which we may have very limited knowledge.

4–6. A DECISION PROBLEM

In this section we will apply some of the concepts that we have been discussing to the solution of some practical sorts of problems. The problems are, of course, highly simplifed but they do serve to illustrate some of the sorts of problems that we are now equipped to solve.

Example 4–13

Suppose, in relation to our distribution of daily demand for a product, that the cost per unit of the product to the retailer is $2 and that the retail price is $3, so that the profit per unit is $1. Suppose for simplicity that there are no other costs that need to be considered and assume that, since the product is perishable, every unit of the product not sold in a given day is a total loss. Then we can construct a *payoff table* or *payoff matrix* as follows to show the net profit to be obtained for each possible stock level from zero through five, and for each possible daily demand over the same range (payoff or profit *M* resulting from stocking *y* units of product if *x* units are demanded):

Number Demanded		Number Stocked (y)					
(x)	0	1	2	3	4	5
0	0	−2	−4	−6	−8	−10
1	0	1	−1	−3	−5	− 7
2	0	1	2	0	−2	− 4
3	0	1	2	3	1	− 1
4	0	1	2	3	4	2
5 or more	0	1	2	3	4	5

Negative values in the table mean, of course, that losses are incurred. What we want to do now is to determine what would be the optimum number of units of the product for our retailer to stock. We consider the optimum number to stock to be that number which will either *maximize the expected gain* or *minimize the expected loss* as the case may be. This then will be our basic decision rule. Whichever stock level either maximizes our expected gains or minimizes the expected losses is the level we will maintain. We recognize, of course, that on a given day we may have a surplus, or we may have a greater demand than we are equipped to take care of. However, since the demand on any given day is unpredictable, the rule that we have decided on will be the best one over the long run. The following table, then, applies the probabilities previously used for this distribution to the payoff matrix to determine the expected profit *M* of each of the alternative stock levels.

x	f(x)	Number Stocked (y)					
		0	1	2	3	4	5
0	.3679	0	−2	−4	−6	−8	−10
1	.3679	0	1	−1	−3	−5	− 7
2	.1839	0	1	2	0	−2	− 4
3	.0613	0	1	2	3	1	− 1
4	.0153	0	1	2	3	4	2
5	.0037	0	1	2	3	4	5

$E(M)$ 0   −.1037   −1.3111   −3.0702   −4.9632   −7.0012

In this case the best that our retailer can do is not to stock any
of the product. Otherwise, he will on the average suffer a loss at
any stock level. To illustrate how the expected values are calcu-
lated, we will calculate the expected value of action $y = 2$
(stocking two units of the product). Namely,

$$E(M) = 4(.3679) - 1(.3679) + 2(.1839 + .0613 + .0153 + .0037)$$
$$= -5(.3679) + 2(.2642) = 1.3111 .$$

Example 4–14

Suppose now (for the same problem as in Example 4–13) that
the probabilities of each of the possible demands were as in the
following table rather than as previously assumed:

x	f(x)	Number Stocked (y)					
		0	1	2	3	4	5
0	$\frac{1}{32}$	0	−2	−4	−6	−8	−10
1	$\frac{5}{32}$	0	1	−1	−3	−5	− 7
2	$\frac{10}{32}$	0	1	2	0	−2	− 4
3	$\frac{10}{32}$	0	1	2	3	1	− 1
4	$\frac{5}{32}$	0	1	2	3	4	2
5	$\frac{1}{32}$	0	1	2	3	4	5

$E(M)$ 0 $\frac{29}{32}$ $\frac{43}{32}$ $\frac{27}{32}$ $\frac{19}{32}$ $\frac{80}{32}$

In this case, the maximum expected profit ($\$^{43}\!/_{32}$) per day
results from stocking two units of the product daily.

It should be fairly clear from these examples that the optimum course of action in any given business situation depends not only on the possible outcomes of alternative actions, but just as importantly on the probabilities of those outcomes. Since nothing in business or in any other phase of life can be predicted with certainty, the application of appropriate probabilities of the outcomes of alternative possible courses of action can lead to significantly improved business decisions over the long run.

Example 4–15

Before leaving this topic let us examine one more example which is probably fairly representative of the kinds of problems that business men often face, and of how what we have covered might help them to come to a decision. Suppose that a general contractor is considering whether or not he should submit a bid for a particular project. The best he can figure, he feels that he can make a profit of about $50,000 with a probability of about .70, or he might make a loss of up to $10,000 with a probability of about .30 as a result of bad weather, labor problems, and other possible delays. This, however, depends on whether or not he gets the contract. It will cost him $1,000 to prepare estimates of costs and to prepare a bid, regardless of whether or not he gets the contract. Our contractor feels that if his closest competitor does not submit a bid, his probability of getting the contract is about .45. On the other hand, if this particular competitor does submit a bid, his probability of getting the contract is only .30. He feels that the probability that the competitor will submit a bid on this contract is about .5. Should he bother to submit a bid?

In order to analyze this problem and help our contractor friend to come to a decision, let us first observe the courses of action open to him and the possible results of those courses of action. If no bid is submitted, nothing can be gained and nothing lost, so the expected value of this course of action is zero. The alternative course of action is to submit a bid. In this case there are three possible outcomes. One is that our friend will not get the contract and will be out $1,000 for the cost of preparing the bid. The second is that he might get the contract and lose the $10,000 in addition to the $1,000 cost of the bid. Finally, he might get the contract and make the $50,000 profit, less the $1,000 cost of preparing the bid. Now let us identify symbolically the various probability components of the problem. Suppose we call G the event of making the profit, L the event of a loss, C the event that our friend gets the contract, and B the event that his competitor bids on the contract. Then the basic probabilities given in the problem are

$$P(G|C) = .70$$
$$P(L|C) = .30$$
$$P(C|B) = .30$$
$$P(C|\overline{B}) = .45$$
$$P(B) = .50.$$

Now, the expected value of a bid in this case is

$$E(M) = \$50,000\ P(G \cap C) - \$10,000\ P(L \cap C) - \$1,000\,.$$

Recall that

$$P(G \cap C) = P(G|C)P(C),$$

by the rules of conditional probabilities. We do not know $P(C)$ directly, but it can be determined as follows:

$$P(C) = P(C|B)P(B) + P(C|\overline{B})P(\overline{B})$$
$$= (.30)(.50) + (.45)(.50) = .375\,.$$

Hence,

$$P(G \cap C) = (.70)(.375) = .2625\,.$$

Similarly,

$$P(L \cap C) = P(L|C)P(C)$$
$$= (.30)(.375) = .1125\,.$$

So the expected profit is

$$E(M) = \$50,000(.2625) - \$10,000(.1125) - \$1,000$$
$$= \$13,125 - \$1,125 - \$1,000$$
$$= \$11,000\,.$$

Thus, our friend could expect on the average under the same conditions to make $11,000 profit, and could thus be expected to go ahead and submit a bid.

Let us now suppose that our friend, the contractor, has learned that his major competitor is definitely submitting a bid. Would this make a difference in the decision? It could. It will be necessary to compute the expected value of the bid again under the new conditions. In this case, the event B is known to have occurred. So,

$$P(C) = P(C|B) = .30, \text{ and}$$
$$P(G \cap C) = (.70)(.30) = .21,$$
$$P(L \cap C) = (.30)(.30) = .09, \text{ and}$$
$$E(M) = \$50{,}000(.21) - \$10{,}000(.09) - \$1{,}000$$
$$= \$10{,}500 - \$900 - \$1{,}000$$
$$= \$8{,}400$$

The expected value is less now, considering that the chances of getting the contract in the first place are less than before. Still, however, the analysis shows that this would be a worthwhile venture, unless there is another project which could be done if this one is not and which has a higher expected value.

Exercises

1. Set up in tabular form the distribution of a random variable X which represents the number of dots on the toss of three dice.
2. Find the expected value and variance of the distribution in Problem one.
3. Six poker chips are numbered 1,2,3,4,5,6, respectively. If X is the random variable denoting the sum of the numbers on two chips drawn at random, set up in tabular form the probability distribution of the random variable.
4. Find the expected value and the variance of the distribution in Problem 3.

(Ans. $E(X) = 3.5$)

5. Suppose a hand of 13 cards is dealth from an ordinary deck of 52 playing cards. Let X be the random variable denoting the number of aces in the hand. Set up in tabular form the probability distribution of X. Derive a general expression for $f(x)$.
6. There is a lot of 10 articles, 2 of which are defective. Suppose that 3 items are selected at random from the lot. Let X be a random variable denoting the number of defective items in the sample, and set up in tabular form the probability distribution of X. Derive a general expression for $f(x)$.
7. Suppose that a person has one of 45,000 tickets, from which 1

will be selected for a prize of $300. What is the value of the ticket?

(Ans. $.67)

8. A particular automobile race driver has 3 chances in 10 of winning a particular race. If the winner is to receive $3,000, what is his expectation?

(Ans. $900)

9. In a lottery 2 drawings are to be made. An automobile worth $3,500 is to be the prize on the first drawing, and a boat complete with motor and trailer with a total value of $2,500 is to be the prize on the second. If a man has 7 of 20,000 tickets on the car and 10 of 15,000 on the boat, what is the probability that he will win either the car or the boat? What is the probability that he will win both? What is his expectation?

10. Of 1,000 raffle tickets, the first prize is worth $200; each of 3 second prizes is worth $50; and each of 10 third prizes is worth $20. If each ticket costs $2, what is the expected net return on one ticket?

11. A firm is considering insuring a new manufacturing plant valued at $300,000. According to local fire mortality rates the estimated probabilty that the plant will be destroyed by fire during the next year is .005. If the annual insurance premium is $2,000, what would be the expected value of a decision to insure? Should the firm insure the plant or not at this premium rate? Suppose a premium rate of $1,400 was offered. What would the expected value be in this case? Would this change your decision?

12. Suppose that from past experience you know that the mean number of defective items in a lot of 50 produced by a particular manufacturer is 2 and that the variance is 4, but you have no information about the probability distribution of the number of defectives. Approximately what is the probability that a particular lot has more than 4 defective items?

(Ans. zero)

13. Suppose that a contractor has his choice of two jobs. He can take either one but because of limitations of capacity and short deadlines he cannot handle both of them. The first job offers a potential profit of $65,000 with a probability of .75 or a potential loss of $15,000 with a probability of .25. The second job offers a potential profit of $90,000 with a probability of .60 and a potential loss of $20,000 with a probability of .40. Which of the two jobs should the contractor choose to maximize his expected gain?

14. A florist who caters to a rather exclusive clientele is faced with the problem of determining the quantity of a particular rare type of orchid to order. He can receive fresh shipments once a week and, if those on hand are not sold within a week, they must be thrown away when the new shipment comes in. This particular orchid costs our florist $6 each and he sells them at a retail price of $15 each. On the basis of past records he determines that weekly demand in the past has had the following relative frequency distribution. On the basis of the relative frequency approach to probability, we will assume this to be the probability distribution of weekly demands:

x	2	3	4	5	6	7	8	9
f(x)	.08	.15	.18	.20	.12	.12	.10	.05

Set up a payoff table for alternative courses of action and calculate the expected payoffs or profits for each of these. What is the optimum number to order?

Selected References

Adams, J. K., *Basic Statistical Concepts,* New York: McGraw-Hill Book Company, Inc., 1956.

Mood, A. M., and F. A. Graybill, *Introduction to the Theory of Statistics,* New York: McGraw-Hill Book Company, Inc., 1963.

Schlaifer, R., *Probability and Statistics for Business Decisions,* New York: McGraw-Hill Book Company, Inc., 1959.

Wilks, S. S., *Elementary Statistical Analysis,* Princeton, N. J.: Princeton University Press, 1949.

chapter five

Probability of a Sample from a Finite Two-Valued Set—the Hypergeometric Distribution

In the last chapter we discussed the nature and usefulness of discrete probability distributions in general. In this chapter and the next two we will take up in some detail three of the most important probability distributions of discrete random variables. These three are the most important both on theoretical and practical grounds. Much of the theory of continuous probabilities will be based in large measure on these distributions. Moreover, there are many practical business situations to which each of the distributions presented here is applicable.

5–1. DERIVATION OF THE DISTRIBUTION

In Chapter 2 of this book there is a discussion of the problem of counting the number of ways of partitioning a set S with a finite number of elements N into two subsets: A, containing n elements; and $\overline{A}$, containing $N - n$ elements. The number of ways in which this can be done was found to be

$$\binom{N}{n} = \frac{N!}{n!\,(N - n)!}$$

Here we want to determine the probability that such a partition satisfies the additional condition that A contains x elements of another subset B (with N_1 elements) of S and $n - x$ elements from the subset $\overline{B}$ (with $N - N_1$ elements). Stated differently, we want to know the probability that n objects selected randomly without replacement from N will be such that x of the n will be selected from the subset B (with N_1 elements) and that $n - x$ of the n will be from the disjoint subset $\overline{B}$ (with $N - N_1$ elements).

Example 5–1

We want to know the probability that if we select without replacement 4 screws from a lot of 12, of which 2 are defective, our sample of 4 will contain 2 screws that are defective.

As we know, the probability of selecting x elements from the subset B and $n - x$ elements from $\overline{B}$ is given by the ratio of the number of ways that this result can occur to the total possible number of outcomes of the selection of n elements from N. As we have already seen, the total number of possible outcomes of the selection of n elements from N is

$$\binom{N}{n} = \frac{N!}{n!\,(N - n)!}$$

This is the denominator in the ratio for computation of the probability. Similarly, the number of possible ways of selecting x objects from the N_1 in the subset B is

$$\binom{N_1}{x} - \frac{N_1!}{x!\,(N_1 - x)!}$$

and the number of ways of selecting $n - x$ elements from the $N - N_1$ in the subset $\overline{B}$ is

$$\binom{N - N_1}{n - x} = \frac{(N - N_1)!}{(n - x)! \cdot [(N - N_1) - (n - x)]!}.$$

Since selection of the x elements from the subset B and $n - x$ elements from subset $\overline{B}$ are independent for a given value of x

and for a given partition $(B,\overline{B})$ of the set S, the total number of ways of selecting x elements from B and $n - x$ elements from $\overline{B}$ is given by the product

$$\binom{N_1}{x} \cdot \binom{N - N_1}{n - x}.$$

This product represents the numerator of the ratio defining the probability that we seek. Thus, combining these various components, the probability of obtaining x elements from subset B and $n - x$ from $\overline{B}$ is

$$P(X = x) = \frac{\binom{N_1}{x} \cdot \binom{N - N_1}{n - x}}{\binom{N}{n}}.$$

This may be stated somewhat more succinctly as

$$h(x) = \frac{\binom{N_1}{x} \cdot \binom{N - N_1}{n - x}}{\binom{N}{n}}, \qquad (5-1)$$

where $h(x)$ is used to denote the hypergeometric density function.

Equation 5–1 is the general term of the hypergeometric probability density function. This gives the probability of obtaining exactly x elements from the subset B in a sample (without replacement) of n elements from a set S containing a finite number N of elements.

Example 5–2

Consider again the problem of Example 5–1. There we wanted to know the probability of obtaining 2 defective screws in a sample of 4 selected from a set of 12 screws of which 2 are defective. Here, $N = 12$, $N_1 = 2$, $n = 4$, and $x = 2$. Substituting into Equation 5–1 gives

$$h(2) = \frac{\binom{2}{2} \times \binom{10}{2}}{\binom{12}{4}} = \frac{12}{132}.$$

In this example, it should be clear that the possible values of our random variable X are zero, one, and two; X cannot be greater than two since N_1, the number of defective elements in the universe set S, is only 2. The probabilities of these other two possible outcomes are

$$h(1) = \frac{\binom{2}{1} \times \binom{10}{3}}{\binom{12}{4}} = \frac{64}{132}.$$

$$h(0) = \frac{\binom{2}{0} \times \binom{10}{4}}{\binom{12}{4}} = \frac{56}{132}.$$

Two very important features of the hypergeometric distribution can be seen immediately from this simple example. The first is that $0 \leq x \leq n$ if $n \leq N_1$, but $0 \leq x \leq N_1$ if $n > N_1$. That is to say, if the number to be selected in the sample (n) is larger than the number of elements in the subset B (N_1), then X can take on all integer values between zero and N_1 inclusive. On the other hand, if $n \leq N_1$, then X can take on all integer values between zero and n inclusive; X can take on as its maximum value either n or N_1, whichever is smaller. The second of the two features of the hypergeometric distribution referred to above, a feature which is common to all three discrete probability distributions covered in this book, is

$$\sum_{x=0}^{m} h(x) = 1, \qquad (5\text{--}2)$$

where m is the maximum possible value of X. In the present case, $m = n$ if $n < N_1$, or $m = N_1$ otherwise.

Example 5–3

In Example 5–2, $(n = 4)$ and $(N_1 = 2)$, so $m = 2$ and

$$\sum_{x=0}^{2} h(x) = h(0) + h(1) + h(2)$$

$$= \frac{56}{132} + \frac{64}{132} + \frac{12}{132} = \frac{132}{132} = 1.$$

Example 5–4

Suppose that the auditors of a particular department store check a sample of 10 of the store's 100 credit accounts. If 3 per cent of the store's accounts contain errors, what is the probability that no more than 1 of the selected accounts will contain errors? Here, we want to find $h(0)$ and $h(1)$. We are given that $N = 100$, $n = 10$, and $N = 3$. Then

$$h(0) = \frac{\binom{3}{0} \times \binom{97}{10}}{\binom{100}{10}} = \frac{178}{245}.$$

$$h(1) = \frac{\binom{3}{1} \times \binom{97}{9}}{\binom{100}{10}} = \frac{267}{1078}.$$

Now, in order to combine these two it is necessary that they have a common denominator. Their common denominator is 5390. So,

$$h(0) = \frac{3916}{5390},$$

and

$$h(1) = \frac{1335}{5390}.$$

Hence, the probability that not more than one of the accounts will be in error is

$$P(X \le 1) = h(0) + h(1) = \frac{3916}{5390} + \frac{1335}{5390} \cong .79 .$$

Conversely, the probability of selecting more than one account which is in error is

$$P(X > 1) = 1 - P(X \le 1) = 1 - .79 = .21 .$$

5–2. AN ITERATIVE COMPUTATIONAL FORMULA

The last example is illustrative of the computational difficulty of applying the hypergeometric density function where even moderately large numbers are involved, and especially where X differs much from zero or its maximum value. Appendix Table I can be used for values of the upper component of the combinatorial notations up to 20, but not for larger values. In addition, there are tables available for $h(x)$ for selected values of N, N_1, and n. Computations can be facilitated somewhat by use of Equation 5–3, however, when appropriate tabular values are not available.

$$h(x) = \frac{(N_1 - x + 1) \cdot (n - x + 1)}{x \cdot [(N - N_1) - (n - x)]} \cdot h(x - 1)$$

(5–3)

Given the value of $h(0)$, then $h(1)$, $h(2)$, etc. can be determined iteratively by repetitive application of Equation 5–3. The proof of Equation 5–3 will be left as an exercise for the student.

Example 5–5

Consider Example 5–4. Given that $h(0) = 178/245$,

$$h(1) = \frac{3 \times 10}{1 \times 88} \times \frac{178}{245} = \frac{30 \times 178}{88 \times 245} = \frac{5340}{21690}$$

$$= \frac{267}{1078}.$$

Similarly, the probability that $X = 2$ is

$$h(2) = \frac{2 \times 9}{2 \times 89} \times \frac{267}{1078} = \frac{2403}{95942} = .025 .$$

5–3. THE EXPECTED VALUE OF X

As indicated in Chapter 4, the expected value of a probability distribution is given by

$$E(X) = \sum_{i=1}^{n} x_i f(x_i),$$

where x is the ith value of X and there are n values of X. In the case of the hypergeometric distribution X can take on all values from zero to n, assuming that $n < N_1$. Thus, the expected value of x for the hypergeometric distribution is

$$E(X) = \sum_{x=0}^{n} xh(x) = \sum_{x=0}^{n} x \cdot \frac{\binom{N_1}{x} \cdot \binom{N - N_1}{n - x}}{\binom{N}{n}}.$$

(5–4)

By some algebraic manipulation and simplification, Equation 5–4 can be reduced to

$$E(X) = \frac{nN_1}{N}.$$

Let us now define $p = N_1/N$. Then the expected value of X where X has a hypergeometric distribution is

$$E(X) = \mu = np. \qquad (5\text{–}5)$$

Example 5–6

In Example 5–4 we found that $p = .03$ and $n = 10$. Hence if we were to take a large number of samples of ten accounts from the store's accounting records, we would expect that on the average there would be .3 accounts containing errors. In our earlier example of the sampling of 4 screws from a box of 12 containing 2 which are defective, the expected number of defective screws in the sample is $\frac{4}{6}$ or .67.

5–4. THE VARIANCE OF X

The expected value of a distribution is the value which can be expected to occur "on the average." As was shown earlier, however, the expected value cannot be expected to occur on every trial or for every sample. In fact, as was also seen earlier, there are many cases in which the expected value can never occur. Hence, the variance of the distribution is very useful as a measure of the dispersion of the values of X about its expected value. It will be remembered, for example, that according to Tchebysheff's theorem, the probability that X will differ from its expected value by more than $\alpha \sigma$ (where σ is the square root of the variance) is not more than $(1/\alpha)^2$.

Thus, it would be helpful to know the variance of the hypergeometric distribution. Knowing the variance, it is possible to approximate hypergeometric probabilities roughly by Tchebysheff's theorem or more precisely by use of other probability distributions to be taken up later in this book.

As shown in Chapter 4, the variance of a distribution is given by

$$\sigma^2 = E(X^2) - \left[E(X)\right]^2. \qquad (5\text{–}6)$$

The second term on the right side of Equation 5–6 is just the square of the expected value of X as already determined. The first term is

$$E(X^2) = \sum_{x=0}^{n} x^2 \cdot h(x)$$

$$= \sum_{x=0}^{n} x^2 \cdot \frac{\binom{N_1}{x} \cdot \binom{N-N_1}{n-x}}{\binom{N}{n}}. \tag{5–7}$$

Again, by considerable algebraic manipulation, Equation 5–7 can be reduced to

$$E(X^2) = \frac{N_1(N_1 - 1)n(n - 1)}{N(N - 1)} + \frac{nN_1}{N} \tag{5–8}$$

Substituting the results of Equations 5–7 and 5–8 into Equation 5–6, we have

$$\sigma^2 = \frac{N_1(N_1 - 1)n(n - 1)}{N(N - 1)} + \frac{nN_1}{N} - \left(\frac{nN_1}{N}\right)^2$$

$$= \frac{nN_1 (N - N_1) (N - n)}{NN (N - 1)}$$

Since we have defined $p = N_1/N$, this becomes

$$\sigma^2 = npq \left(\frac{N - n}{N - 1}\right), \tag{5–9}$$

where $q = 1 - p$.

Thus, with Equation 5–9 we can compute the variance of a hypergeometric distribution without ever computing the probabilities of all outcomes.

Example 5–7

The variance of the number of accounts in error in our preceding example is

$$\sigma^2 = 10 \times (.03) \times (.97) \times \left(\frac{90}{99}\right) = .2645 .$$

We found earlier that the expected number of accounts in error is .3. Hence, according to Tchebysheff's theorem, we would expect that the probability that the actual number of accounts in error in any given sample differs from .3 by more than approximately one account is not more than $\frac{1}{4}$. Here, α was assumed to be equal to 2 and σ equal to .5 approximately.

Example 5–8

In our example of sampling for defective screws from a box of 12 screws of which two are defective, the variance is

$$\sigma^2 = 4 \times \left(\frac{1}{6}\right) \times \left(\frac{5}{6}\right) \times \left(\frac{8}{11}\right) = .404 .$$

Applying Tchebysheff's theorem to this, the probability that the number of defective screws in the sample differs from .67 (the expected number) by more than 1.24 is not greater than .25. Actually, these probabilities, for the hypergeometric distribution, are considerably less than .25. As we have already seen, Tchebysheff's theorem only provides an indication of the maximum probability that X will differ from μ by more than $\alpha \sigma$.

Example 5–9

Suppose that in a city of 10,000 people, 30 per cent of the people read a particular newspaper. If we take a sample of 200 people, the expected number in the sample who read this newspaper is

$$\mu = 200 \times (.30) = 60 .$$

The variance is

$$\sigma^2 = 200 \times (.30) \times (.70) \times \left(\frac{9800}{9999}\right) = 41.2 ,$$

and the standard deviation is

$$\sigma \cong 6.25 .$$

Using Tchebysheff's theorem as an approximation again, the probability is not more than .25 that the number of people in the sample group who read the newspaper of interest differs from 60 by more than 12.5. Stated differently, the probability is at least .75 that the number in the sample who read this newspaper is between about 48 and 72. Very likely, this probability is substantially greater than .75.

5–5. EXTENSION TO SETS OF MORE THAN TWO VALUES

It is easy to imagine problem situations which satisfy the conditions leading to the development of the hypergeometric distribution but which have more than two possible outcomes on each trial. That is, whereas we have assumed that we were sampling from a set S which was partitioned into two subsets B and $\overline{B}$, we can visualize the problem of sampling from a set S which has been partitioned into any number of subsets. Suppose, for example, that S has been partitioned into four disjoint and exhaustive subsets A, B, C, and D, each containing, respectively, W, X, Y, and Z elements such that $N = N_1 + N_2 + N_3 + N_4$. Then the probability that a sample of n elements selected from S without replacement will contain exactly w elements from subset A, x elements from subset B, y elements from subset C, and z elements from subset D is given by

$$f(w,x,y,z) \;=\; \frac{\binom{N_1}{w} \cdot \binom{N_2}{x} \cdot \binom{N_3}{y} \cdot \binom{N_4}{z}}{\binom{N}{n}}. \tag{5-10}$$

Equation 5–10 is an extension of Equation 5–1 to more than two possible outcomes. Equation 5–10 can easily be extended to any number of possible outcomes on each sample selection. For the equation to apply, however, it is necessary that the possible subsets of S be disjoint *and* exhaustive.

Example 5–10

Suppose that we have a certain class which comprises 10 freshmen, 8 sophomores, 6 juniors, and 3 seniors. Suppose now that we are to select at random a committee of 8 students from the 27 in the class. What is the probability that it will comprise exactly 2 of each of the 4 classifications? This is given by

$$f(2,2,2,2) \;=\; \frac{\binom{10}{2} \times \binom{8}{2} \times \binom{6}{2} \times \binom{3}{2}}{\binom{27}{8}} \;=\; \frac{420}{3289}.$$

Exercises

1. Prove the correctness of Equation 5–3.

2. Show that $h(x) = h(n - x)$ if and only if $N_1 = N - N_1$.

3. A committee of the student government consists of ten male and eight female students. If a subcommittee of five members is chosen by drawing lots, what is the probability that the sub-committee will comprise (a) five females, (b) five males, (c) two males and three females, (d) at least two males, (e) not more than four males?

4. Among the 25 members of the board of directors of a particular company, 9 are in favor of opening a foreign branch of the company, 10 are opposed, and the rest are undecided. If a committee of 5 is chosen at random to make the final decision on the basis of a majority vote, what is the probability that the branch will be opened (a) assuming that the undecideds will abstain and their votes will not count for or against, (b) assuming that the undecideds will vote with the majority of those who have made up their minds, (c) assuming that the undecideds will vote with the minority of those who have made up their minds, (d) assuming that the undecideds will vote for opening the foreign branch with a probability equal to the ratio of favorable votes to the total decided votes on the committee?

5. If five cards are dealt from a deck of ordinary playing cards, what is the probability that (a) none of the five is red, (b) one is red, (c) two are red, (d) three are red, (e) two are aces, (f) four are clubs?

(Ans. [a] $253/9996$)

6. A box of 12 photographic flash bulbs contains 1 bulb which is defective. If 3 bulbs are selected at random from the box, what are the possible values of X where X is the number of defective bulbs selected? What are the probabilities of these values of X?

7. Suppose that in a class of 30 students, 10 fail their first test of the semester. If 8 people are selected at random from the class, what is the probability that 4 of these failed the exam? What is the probability that not more than 3 failed the exam?

8. In a central secretarial pool there are 10 secretaries. Of these only 3 can type faster than 65 words a minute. If 2 are selected at random for a particular typing job, what is the probability

that both of them can type faster than 65 words a minute? What is the probability that neither of them type this fast?

(Ans. $\frac{1}{15}$; $\frac{21}{45}$)

Selected References

Adams, J. K., *Basic Statistical Concepts,* New York: McGraw-Hill Book Company, Inc., 1956.

Feller, W., *Introduction to Probability Theory and Its Application,* Vol. I, 2nd. ed., New York: John Wiley & Sons, Inc., 1957.

Fruend, J. E., *Mathematical Statistics,* Englewood Cliffs, N. J.: Prentice-Hall, Inc., 1962.

Goldberg, S., *Probability — An Introduction,* Englewood Cliffs, N. J.: Prentice-Hall, Inc., 1960.

Mood, A. M., and F. A. Graybill, *Introduction to the Theory of Statistics,* New York. McGraw-Hill Book Company, Inc., 1963.

Wilks, S. S., *Elementary Statistical Analysis,* Princeton, N. J.: Princeton University Press, 1949.

chapter six

Independent Trials with Two Outcomes — the Binomial Distribution

6–1. DERIVATION OF THE BINOMIAL DENSITY FUNCTION

In the last chapter we examined in some detail the probability distribution resulting from the selection of n elements from among N without replacement after each selection. There we derived the hypergeometric probability density function $h(x)$, the probability that the sample of n elements selected will include exactly x which are members of the subset A of the universe set containing N_1 elements. Let us assume now that we select n elements from the same finite universe set containing N_1 elements in subset A and $N - N_1$ elements in the disjoint subset B. Let us suppose this time though that we select one element at a time, replacing the element each time before the next one is selected. Thus, the outcome of each selection is independent of the outcomes on all other selections.

If we define the ratio

$$p = \frac{N_1}{N}$$

to be the probability of selecting an element from subset A on any given selection, then it should be clear that p remains constant over all n selections. Then, too,

$$1 - p = \frac{N - N_1}{N}$$

is the probability that an element from subset B (or "not A") will be selected on any given selection.

Example 6–1

Suppose that we draw five marbles (one at a time, replacing and mixing before the next selection) from a bag containing six red and four black marbles all of equal size and weight. What is the probability that we will draw first three red and then two black marbles? That is, we want to know the joint probability of occurrence of first three red and then two black marbles in five independent trials. Following the rule for determining joint probabilities of independent events as presented in Chapter 2, this probability would be

$$(.6) \times (.6) \times (.6) \times (.4) \times (.4) = (.6)^3 \times (.4)^2$$
$$\cong .03 .$$

Now, what is the probability of first selecting two black marbles and then three red ones? Following the same reasoning, this would be

$$(.4) \times (.4) \times (.6) \times (.6) \times (.6) = (.4)^2 \times (.6)^3$$
$$\cong .03 .$$

Similarly, the probability of selecting first one red marble, then two black ones, and then two more red ones is

$$(.6) \times (.4) \times (.4) \times (.6) \times (.6) = (.6)^3 \times (.4)^2$$
$$\cong .03 .$$

Thus, for every possible arrangement of three red and two black marbles, the probability is the same.

Suppose that we want to know, then, the probability of selecting exactly three red and two black marbles from this bag under
the conditions outlined (without regard to the order of selection).
This would be given by summing the probabilities of each possible arrangement of three red and two black marbles. However,
each of these has the same probability [namely, $(.6)^3 \times (.4)^2$]
and there are $\binom{5}{3}$ such arrangements. Therefore, the probability
of obtaining exactly three red and two black marbles is

$$\binom{5}{3} \times (.6)^3 \times (.4)^2 = (10) \times (.03) = .3.$$

Stating the problem in Example 6–1 more generally, we want to
know the probability of obtaining exactly x elements from set A and
$n - x$ from set "not A" when selecting n elements from the universe
set S with N_1 of its N elements in the subset A. Again, with each
selection being made one at a time *with* replacement after each
selection, the probability of first getting x elements from subset A
and then $n - x$ elements from "not A" is

$$\underbrace{ppp \ldots p}_{x \text{ times}} \underbrace{(1 - p)(1 - p) \ldots (1 - p)}_{n - x \text{ times}}$$

$$= p^x(1 - p)^{n-x} = p^x q^{n-x}$$

where $q = 1 - p$.

Every possible arrangement of exactly x elements from subset A
and $n - x$ elements from subset "not A" has this same probability
and there are $\binom{n}{x}$ such arrangements. Thus, the probability of
obtaining exactly x elements from the subset A without regard to the
particular arrangement of A's and not A's is

$$P(X=x) = b(x) = \binom{n}{x} p^x \cdot q^{n-x}. \qquad (6\text{--}1)$$

Equation 6–1 is the general term of the binomial probability density
function. Given the value of p, this measures the probability of
obtaining exactly x elements from the subset A on a selection of
n elements for all integer values of x such that $0 \le x \le n$. Appendix
Table II contains values of $b(x)$ for selected values of n and p.

The basic conditions which must exist for the binomial density
function to apply are: (1) the outcome on each selection must be
independent of the outcomes on each prior and each subsequent
selection, (2) there must be two mutually exclusive possible out-

comes on each selection, and (3) each selection must be made under the same conditions throughout the selection process (i.e., the value of p must remain constant). A sequence of selections made under these conditions is defined to be an experiment comprising a sequence of *Bernoulli* trials.

In this particular case we assumed that we were selecting physical objects from a finite set of such objects, each having one or the other of two possible characteristics. Such an assumption is not necessary. There need not be a finite number of objects from which we select physically. We might, for example, toss a coin several times and count the number of times heads turn up. For such an "experiment" to constitute a sequence of Bernoulli trials, however, the probability of head on each toss (p) must remain the same for all tosses — we must not learn to control the outcome of a toss or modify the value of p in any way. In this case, there is no physical finite universe set from which we are selecting with replacement. There are an infinite number of possible tosses of the coin and the outcome of each toss is independent of the outcomes on all others.

6–2. GENERAL CHARACTERISTICS OF THE DISTRIBUTION

Like the hypergeometric distribution, the binomial distribution is a distribution of a discrete random variable X. In the case of the binomial distribution, however, both N and N_1 (the number of elements in the universe set and in the subset A) are treated as if they are infinite. There is no limit as to the number of times that a coin might be tossed or the number of times that a head might turn up. In the case of selection of marbles from a bag, neither N nor N_1 is infinite in reality; but, since the marble selected is replaced each time before the next selection is made, the process can be repeated indefinitely. Hence, in effect, we may treat the process as one of selection from an infinite universe. Whereas the range of possible values of X for the hypergeometric distribution depends on whether $N_1 < n$ or $N_1 > n$, N_1 is considered conceptually to be infinitely large, hence $N_1 \geq n$. Thus, X can take on all integer values such that $0 \leq X \leq n$.

It was seen earlier that $\binom{n}{x} = \binom{n}{n-x}$ for any permissible value of X, so that the coefficient of the general term of the binomial distribution is symmetric about the central term of the expansion

$$\sum_{x=0}^{n} \binom{n}{x} \cdot p^x q^{n-x} = \binom{n}{0} \cdot q^n + \binom{n}{1} \cdot p \cdot q^{n-1}$$

$$+ \ldots \binom{n}{n} \cdot p^n = 1. \tag{6-2}$$

There are $n + 1$ terms in the expansion represented by Equation 6–2. If $p = .5$, the product $p^x q^{n-x}$ is constant for all values of X. Thus, in this case, $b(x) = b(n - x)$, i.e., the value of $b(x)$ is symmetric about the central term of the expansion where it reaches its maximum. Since the number of terms in Equation 6–2 is equal to $n + 1$, if n is an even integer there are an odd number of terms and there is a single central term which is a maximum. If n is odd, there are an even number of terms and two equal central values of the density function.

If, on the other hand, $p < .5$, $b(x) > b(n - x)$ for all values of X such that $x < n - x$. This is easily verified. Hence, for all $p < .5$ the density function is positively skewed. This means that values of the density function are relatively large for small values of X and become very small for large values of X. Such a distribution is illustrated in Figure 6–1. Here, three density functions are shown, each with $n = 5$, but function (a) has $p = .25$, function (b) has $p = .5$, and (c) has $p = .75$. It should be noted that $b(x)$ for $p = .25$ is equal to $b(n - x)$ for $p = .75$. For example, the probability of obtaining two black marbles in our previous example (with the probability of a black marble on each selection equal to .4) is the same as the probability of obtaining three red ones (with the probability of red on each selection equal to .6). This can be stated in more general terms as

$$b(y) = \binom{n}{y} \cdot q^y \cdot p^{n-y} = \binom{n}{x} \cdot p^x \cdot q^{n-x} = b(x),$$

$$\tag{6-3}$$

where $y = n - x$.

6–3. THE EXPECTED VALUE OF X

Just as with the hypergeometric distribution, or any other discrete probability distribution for that matter, the expected value of the binomially distributed variable is given by

$$E(X) = \sum_{x=0}^{n} x b(x) = \sum_{x=0}^{n} x \cdot \binom{n}{x} \cdot p^x \cdot q^{n-x}. \tag{6-4}$$

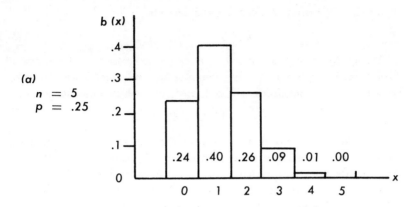

(a)

n = 5
p = .25

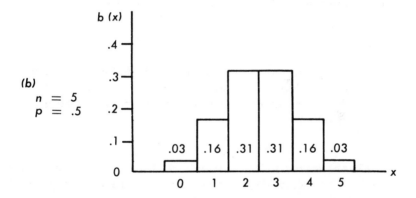

(b)

n = 5
p = .5

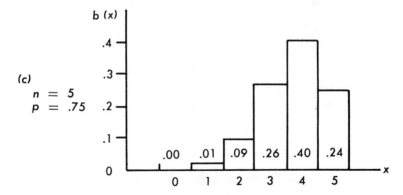

(c)

n = 5
p = .75

FIGURE 6–1. Three Binomial Probability
Distributions for n = 5 and
p = .25, p = .50, and p = .75

105

As with the hypergeometric distribution, a small amount of algebraic simplification reduces Equation 6–4 to

$$E(X) = np = \mu. \tag{6–5}$$

Thus, the expected (or average, or mean) number of red marbles which will appear when five marbles are selected from our bag in Example 6–1 containing six red and four black marbles is

$$\mu = (5) \times (.6) = 3.$$

That is to say, if we were to repeat the experiment of selecting five marbles from our bag a large number of times, we would expect, on the average, three red marbles per selection. Sometimes we would obtain more than three red ones and sometimes fewer. The probability of obtaining any specific number of red (or black) marbles can be determined directly from the density function.

Example 6–2

Let us suppose that we examine at random 10 accounts of a very large department store, 1 per cent of whose accounts are in error. The expected number of erroneous accounts selected among the 10 is

$$\mu = (10) \times (.01) = .1.$$

On the average, there will only be .1 erroneous accounts among the 10 selected. This means, of course, that most of the time none of the selected accounts will be in error, but occasionally there will be one or possibly more in error.

Example 6–3

Suppose that the probability that a telephone number dialed at random is busy is .05. Then, if we dial 50 numbers at random, the expected number of busy signals is

$$\mu = (50) \times (.05) = 2.5.$$

6–4. THE VARIANCE OF X

Although the expected number of "successes" in a given number of trials may be determined easily by Equation 6–5, it is obvious that the numbers which occur on individual trials will vary from trial to trial. We do not always get the expected number of heads on the toss of five coins, nor do we always get the expected number of red marbles or the expected number of erroneous department store accounts or the expected number of busy signals on 50 telephone calls. If the expected value of X always occurred, there would be no uncertainty and our notions of probability would be meaningless and useless. Since X is a random variable, there is variation from the expected value. The variance σ^2 of X is, as we have seen before, a measure of the variability of X. The variance has been defined as

$$\sigma^2 = E(X^2) - [E(X)]^2 = \sum_{x=0}^{n} x^2 \cdot b(x) - \mu^2. \qquad (6\text{--}6)$$

The second term in the extreme right side of Equation 6–6 is

$$\mu^2 = (np)^2.$$

The first term is

$$\sum_{x=0}^{n} x^2 b(x) = \sum_{x=0}^{n} x^2 \cdot \binom{n}{x} p^x \cdot q^{n-x}. \qquad (6\text{--}7)$$

However, Equation 6–7 can be reduced to

$$\sum_{x=0}^{n} x^2 \cdot \binom{n}{x} \cdot p^x q^{n-x} = n(n-1)p^2 + np. \qquad (6\text{--}8)$$

Substituting into Equation 6–6, we get

$$\begin{aligned}
\sigma^2 &= n(n-1)p^2 + np - (np)^2 \\
&= np - np^2 \\
&= np \cdot q. \qquad (6\text{--}9)
\end{aligned}$$

Hence, the variance of the binomially distributed random variable X is very simply equal to the expected value of X multiplied by the factor q. Thus the variance must always be less than the expected value of X, except in the trivial cases where $p = 0$ or $p = 1$.

It should be recalled that the variance of X for the hypergeometric distribution was found to be

$$\sigma^2 = np \cdot q \cdot \left(\frac{N-n}{N-1} \right).$$

This is very similar to Equation 6–9 except for the fraction in parentheses in the last term of the product. It should be clear that for any finite universe set of N elements, this fraction must be equal to or less than one for all $n > 0$. Hence the variance for the hypergeometric distribution for any $n > 1$ is less than the variance for the binomial distribution with the same n. Moreover, for very large N, $\left(\dfrac{N - n}{N - 1}\right)$ is nearly 1, and the variance of the hypergeometric distribution approaches that of the binomial distribution. None of this should be surprising to the student since we have defined the binomial distribution in such a way that we, in effect, assume selection of n elements from an infinitely large universe set.

Example 6–4

In Example 6–1 the variance of the number of red marbles appearing in the selection of five marbles is

$$\sigma^2 = (5) \times (.6) \times (.4) = 1.2 .$$

Example 6–5

The variance in the number of erroneous accounts in a group of 10 selected at random is

$$\sigma^2 = (10) \times (.01) \times (.99) = .099 .$$

Example 6–6

The variance in the number of busy signals when 50 telephone numbers are dialed at random is

$$\sigma^2 = (50) \times (.05) \times (.95) = 2.375 .$$

6–5. RELATION OF THE BINOMIAL AND HYPERGEOMETRIC DISTRIBUTIONS

At this point it should come as no surpise to the student that the hypergeometric and binomial distributions are closely related. After all, they were derived from the same example situation with only slightly different assumptions about the way selections were made. In the previous section we saw the relation between the variances of the two distributions, and in Section 6–3 it was observed that they have the same expected values. Here we will examine this relationship in greater depth and show that in reality as N becomes indefinitely large, the hypergeometric distribution approaches the binomial.

To this end we state, without proof,[1] that

$$N! \cong \sqrt{2\pi N N^N e^{-N}}. \qquad (6\text{--}10)$$

Equation 6–10 is known as Stirling's approximation to the factorial, or simply as Stirling's formula. In Equation 6–10, $\pi \cong 3.14$ (the mathematical constant used in trigonometric functions) and $e \cong 2.718$ (the base of natural logarithms).

According to Equation 5–1, the hypergeometric density function is

$$h(x) = \frac{\binom{N_1}{x} \cdot \binom{N - N_1}{n - x}}{\binom{N}{n}}. \qquad (6\text{--}11)$$

What we want to show is that

$$h(x) \cong b(x)$$

for N very large.

Let us define $p = N_1/N$. Then $N_1 = Np$ and $N - N_1 = N(1 - p) = Nq$. Substituting into Equation 6–11 gives

$$h(x) = \frac{\binom{Np}{x} \cdot \binom{Nq}{n - x}}{\binom{N}{n}} = \frac{n! \, (Np)!(Nq)!(N - n)!}{x!(Np - x)!(n - x)!(Nq - n + x)!N!}$$

$$= \binom{n}{x} \frac{(Np)!(Nq)!(N - n)!}{(Np - x)!(Nq - n + x)!N!}. \qquad (6\text{--}12)$$

Substituting Equation 6–10 for all factorial terms in the right side of Equation 6–12 and simplifying, we have

$$h(x) \cong \binom{n}{x} \frac{p^{Np+1/2} \cdot q^{Nq+1/2} \cdot (1 - n/N)^{N-n+1/2}}{(p - x/N)^{Np-x+1/2} \cdot [q - (n + x)/N]^{Nq-n+x+1/2}}. \qquad (6\text{--}13)$$

Now, as N is allowed to become infinitely large, then x/N, $(n + x)/N$, and n/N each approach zero. Therefore,

---

[1] A proof may be found in J. V. Uspensky, *Introduction to Mathematical Probability* (New York: McGraw-Hill Book Company, Inc., 1937).

$$h(x) \cong \binom{n}{x} p^x \cdot q^{n-x} = b(x). \qquad (6\text{-}14)$$

Hence, as N (the number of elements in the universe set) becomes very large, the outcome of each selection (without replacement as in the development of the hypergeometric distribution) tends to become more nearly independent of the outcomes on prior selections. The value of the hypergeometric density function for any given value of X becomes approximately the same as the value of the binomial density function. Since the binomial density function is easier to use than is the hypergeometric, if N is reasonably large relative to n, the binomial density function may be used as an approximation of the hypergeometric. Moreover, more extensive tables are available for the binomial than for the hypergeometric distribution.

Example 6–7

Suppose that we are to select 10 electric light bulbs from a box containing 20 bulbs, of which 10 are defective. What is the probability of selecting exactly 3 defective bulbs? In this problem $N = 20$, $N_1 = 10$, $n = 10$, and $x = 3$. Using the hypergeometric density function, the exact probability is

$$P(X = 3) = h(3) = \frac{\binom{10}{3} \times \binom{10}{7}}{\binom{20}{10}} \cong .08.$$

Using the binomial density function as an approximation, we get

$$b(3) = \binom{10}{3} \times (.5)^{10} = .119.$$

Let us now change the problem slightly by increasing N to 100 and also increasing N_1 to 50, so that the ratio N_1/N remains constant at .5. Now, what is the probability that a sample of $n = 10$ bulbs selected without replacement will contain exactly 3 defective ones? Using the hypergeometric density function, we obtain

$$h(3) = \frac{\binom{50}{3} \times \binom{50}{7}}{\binom{100}{10}} = .113,$$

which is very nearly equal to the approximate probability obtained above by use of the binomial density function. In general, if N is fairly large (say at least ten times the value of n) the binomial density function will yield an acceptable approximation to the hypergeometric distribution. That is important in view of the ease of calculating binomial probabilities as compared to the hypergeometric, and particularly since there are tables such as Appendix Table II available for binomial probabilities for selected values of n and p.

6–6. THE LAW OF LARGE NUMBERS (BERNOULLI'S THEOREM)

According to Tchebysheff's inequality as developed in Chapter 4, the probability that an observed value of a random variable will differ from its expected value by more than any specified quantity $\alpha \sigma$ is

$$P(|x - \mu| > \alpha\sigma) < \frac{1}{\alpha^2}. \qquad (6\text{–}15)$$

Let us now apply this to the binomial distribution. Recall that for the binomial distribution, $\mu = E(X) = np$ and $\sigma^2 = npq$. Let us define $W = X/n$. This is the sample proportion of "successes." Then

$$E(W) = E\left(\frac{X}{n}\right) = \frac{E(X)}{n} = \frac{np}{n} = p, \qquad (6\text{–}16)$$

and

$$
\begin{aligned}
\sigma_w^2 &= E(W^2) - [E(W)]^2 = E\left[\left(\frac{X}{n}\right)^2\right] - \left[E\left(\frac{X}{n}\right)\right]^2 \\
&= \frac{E(X^2) - E(X)^2}{n^2} = \frac{[E(X^2) - (E(X))^2]}{n^2} \\
&= \frac{\sigma_x^2}{n^2} = \frac{npq}{n^2} \\
&= \frac{pq}{n}. \qquad (6\text{–}17)
\end{aligned}
$$

Equation 6–16 is the expected value of the distribution of sample proportions and Equation 6–17 is the variance. Restating Equation 6–1 in terms of the random variable W, we have

$$P(|W - p| > \alpha\sigma_w) < \frac{1}{\alpha^2}. \qquad (6\text{–}18)$$

If we define an arbitrarily small constant $\lambda = \alpha \, \sigma_w$, and substitute this into Equation 6–18, we have

$$P(|W - p| > \lambda) < \left(\frac{\sigma_w^2}{\lambda^2}\right),$$

or from Equation 6–17

$$P(|W - p| > \lambda) < \left(\frac{pq}{n\lambda^2}\right). \qquad (6-19)$$

Now, as n becomes very large, with p and λ constant, the right side of Equation 6–19 approaches zero. That is to say, for large n,

$$P(|W - p| > \lambda) \cong 0. \qquad (6-20)$$

What Equation 6–20 tells us is that for a large number of trials, the probability that the sample proportion W of "successes" will differ by more than an arbitrarily small constant λ from the true probability of "success" on a given trial p is very nearly zero. Moreover, the larger is the value of n, the smaller is this probability.

Equation 6–20 provides theoretical justification for the relative frequency approach to probability; since by Equation 6–20 an observed value of W is likely to be very nearly equal to p for large n, W may be considered to be the approximate probability of "success" on a given trial.

6–7. EXTENSION TO THE MULTINOMIAL DISTRIBUTION

Example 6–8

Let us now consider a problem similar to the one with which we began this chapter but with more than two possible outcomes on each selection. More specifically, suppose that we have a bag containing 10 marbles, 2 of which are red, 3 of which are black, and 5 of which are white. If we select 5 marbles from the bag one at a time and replace each time before the next selection, what is the probability that the 5 marbles selected will comprise exactly 2 red, 2 black, and 1 white? Following the same reasoning used in the development of the binomial distribution at the beginning of this chapter, we find that the answer is

$$P(X = 2, Y = 2, Z = 1) = f(x, y, z)$$

$$= \frac{5!}{2!2!1!} (.2)^2 \times (.3)^2 \times (.5) = .054 .$$

In general, if n independent selections are made from a universe set S comprising r disjoint subsets, the probability that the n elements selected will comprise exactly x_1 elements from subset A_1, x_2 from subset $A_2, \ldots,$ and x_r elements from A_r (such that $\sum_{i=1}^{r} x_i = n$) is

$$f(x_1, x_2, \ldots x_r) = \frac{n!}{x_1! x_2! \ldots x_r!} \cdot P_1^{x_1} \cdot P_2^{x_2} \cdot \ldots P_r^{x_r}. \qquad (6\text{--}21)$$

In Equation 6–21, p_1 is the probability of selecting an element from subset A_1 on a given selection, p_2 is the probability of selecting an element from $A_2, \ldots,$ and p_r is the probability of selecting an element from A_r.

Moreover, $\sum_{i=1}^{r} p_i = 1$. It should be clear at this point that Equation 6–1 is a special case (where $r = 2$) of Equation 6–21.

6–8. EXTENSION TO THE PASCAL DISTRIBUTION

Example 6–9

Let us go back to our original problem of independent selections from a bag containing six red and four black marbles. Suppose, however, that we are now interested in the number of selections necessary to obtain three red marbles. Our random variable now is N, the number of selections necessary to draw a fixed number x of red marbles. Let us suppose for the present that $x = 3$, and we know that $p = .6$. We want to know the probability that $N = 5$. In effect, we want to know the probability of obtaining two red marbles in four selections, then another red on the fifth selection. By the binomial distribution, the probability of two red marbles on four selections is

$$b(2) = \binom{4}{2} \times (.6)^2 \times (.4)^2.$$

So the probability that we are after is

$$P(N = 5) = P(x = 2) \times (.6)$$
$$= b(2) \times (.6) = \binom{4}{2} \times (.6)^3 \times (.4)^2.$$

In general, the probability that n trials will be necessary to obtain a given number x of "successes" is given by

$$f(n) = \binom{n-1}{x-1} p^r \cdot q^{n-r}, \qquad (6\text{--}22)$$

where p is the probability of "success" on a given trial. Equation 6–22 is known as the *Pascal* probability density function, or is sometimes referred to as the *negative binomial* density function. In Equation 6–22, N must be at least as large as x; it is not possible to have x successes in fewer than x trials.

Example 6–10

Let us suppose that a firm produces photographic flash bulbs and that their productive process is such that 2 per cent of their bulbs are defective. What is the probability that the firm will have to produce 10 bulbs in order to fill an order for 9 good ones? This is given by

$$P(N = 10) = f(10) = \binom{9}{8} \times (.98)^9 \times (.02) \cong .14 .$$

The probability that 9 bulbs must be produced is

$$P(N = 9) = f(9) = \binom{8}{8} \times (.98)^9 \cong .79 .$$

Exercises

1. Prove that $\qquad b(x) = \dfrac{(n - x + 1) \cdot p}{x \cdot q} \cdot b(x - 1) .$

2. Following the procedure outlined in Section 6–5, prove in detail that $h(x) \cong b(x)$ for very large n.

3. Prove that the expected value of N in the Pascal distribution is equal to x/p.

4. Discuss the difference in conditions that must exist in a problem situation for application of the hypergeometric and the binomial distributions.

5. Calculate the value of $b(x)$ for all permissible values of X, given that $n = 5$ and $p = .4$. Calculate the values of this function with $p = .6$. Verify that $b(x)$ in the first of these is equal to

$b(n - x)$ in the second, for all values of X. Verify that $\sum_{x=0}^{n} b(x) = 1$.

6. A particular machine is to be set up to produce a particular product in sequence. Each unit of the product has a fixed but unknown probability p of being defective (as a result of random variations). However, the quality of each individual unit is independent of the quality of those before or after it. If p is high, then the setup is bad and will have to be redone. In order to make a decision as to whether or not p is too high, a sample of n items is selected and a decision is made on the basis of X, the number of defective items in the sample. If $X > c$ the machine will be set up again. Otherwise it will not. In the following situations, what is the probability that the machine will be set up again?

a. $n = 10$, $c = 0$, $p = .05$ b. $n = 10$, $c = 1$, $p = .1$

c. $n = 20$, $c = 0$, $p = .05$ d. $n = 20$, $c = 1$, $p = .1$.

(Ans. [a] $1 - [.95]^{10}$)

7. Calculate binomial approximations to Problems 3 and 4 in Chapter 5.

8. If a balanced coin is tossed 680 times, what are the expected number of heads that will turn up, and the variance of the number of heads?

(Ans. 340; 170)

9. Suppose that an ordinary die is tossed 200 times. What are the expected number and variance of the number of times that a 6 will turn up?

(Ans. $33\frac{1}{3}$; $27\frac{7}{9}$)

10. Assume that approximately 40 per cent of the viewers of a particular television program can recall the sponsor of the program. Suppose that 2,000 of the viewers are selected at random and asked to name the sponsor. What is the expected number who can name the sponsor correctly? What is the variance and standard deviation (square root of the variance)? What is the approximate probability that more than 1,000 of the viewers can name the sponsor correctly (use Tchebysheff's inequality to find the approximation)?

11. Consider two values a and b such that $a < b < p$. What, if anything, does the law of large numbers tell us about $P(a < X/n < b)$ for very large n? Suppose that $a < p < b$. Answer the same question again for this case.

12. Suppose that we have a bag containing 100 marbles, half of which are red. Half of the remaining ones are white, and the rest are

black. If we select 10 marbles from the bag, replacing after each selection, what is the probability of obtaining exactly 3 red, 4 white, and 3 black marbles?

13. If we toss a coin five times, what is the probability that the third head turned up is on the fifth coin tossed?

(Ans. $\frac{3}{16}$)

14. Suppose that a machine producing a particular component part produces 2 per cent defective parts. What is the expected number of parts that will have to be produced to obtain 100 good parts? What is the probability that more than 10 parts will have to be produced to get 8 good ones?

(Ans. 102)

15. Inspection of 2,600 welded joints welded by a particular machine has yielded 280 defective joints. Of the next 6 joints welded by the machine, what are the probabilities of getting 0, 1, 2, 3, 4, 5, or 6 defective joints?

16. A particular firm which sells by direct mail expects to make a sale on 3 per cent of its mailings. Of 10 mailings, what is the probability of making at least 1 sale?

17. In Problem 16, what is the probability that no more than 10 mailings will be necessary to make 1 sale?

18. Prove, in general terms, the validity of Equation 6–22.

Selected References

Adams, J. K., *Basic Statistical Concepts,* New York: McGraw-Hill Book Company, Inc., 1956.

Feller, W., *Introduction to Probability Theory and Its Application,* Vol. I, 2nd. ed., New York: John Wiley & Sons, Inc., 1957.

Freund, J. E., *Mathematical Statistics,* Englewood Cliffs, N. J.: Prentice-Hall, Inc., 1962.

Goldberg, S., *Probability — An Introduction,* Englewood Cliffs, N. J.: Prentice-Hall, Inc., 1960.

Mood, A. M., and F. A. Graybill, *Introduction to the Theory of Statistics,* New York: McGraw-Hill Book Company, Inc., 1963.

Wilks, S. S., *Elementary Statistical Analysis,* Princeton, N. J.: Princeton University Press, 1949.

chapter seven

Discrete Random Variables
in Time or Space—the
Poisson Distribution

7–1. DEFINITION OF THE DISTRIBUTION

The Poisson probability distribution is the distribution of a discrete random variable X which can take on all positive integral values 0, 1, 2, 3, . . . , ∞, where X is the number of occurrences of some event in time or space. Some typical examples of Poisson variates are (1) the number of telephone calls per minute coming into a particular switchboard, (2) the number of misprints per page in a book, (3) the number of bubbles per square inch of plate glass, (4) the number of customers per minute arriving at the check-out counter of a grocery store, (5) the number of automobile accidents per day on a busy stretch of highway, (6) the number of four-leaf clovers per square yard in a clover patch, and (7) the number of breakdowns per week among a battery of machines in a factory.

The Poisson distribution has the following density function

$$f(x) = \frac{\alpha^x e^{-\alpha}}{x!} \tag{7-1}$$

where X is the random variate, $\alpha > 0$ is the parameter of the distribution, and $e \cong 2.718$ is the base of natural logarithms.

The basic conditions leading to the Poisson distribution are (1) that the occurrence or nonoccurrence of an event in any given interval of time or space is independent of its occurrence or nonoccurrence in other intervals, (2) that increasing or decreasing the interval (Δt) of time or space increases or decreases the probability of occurrence of an event proportionately, (3) that Δt can be made small enough so that the probability of two or more occurrences of the event within the interval is near zero, and (4) that the probability of X events in the interval increases or decreases continuously as the interval increases or decreases continuously.

The derivation of Equation 7-1 follows directly from these four conditions. The derivation will be foregone, however, since it requires

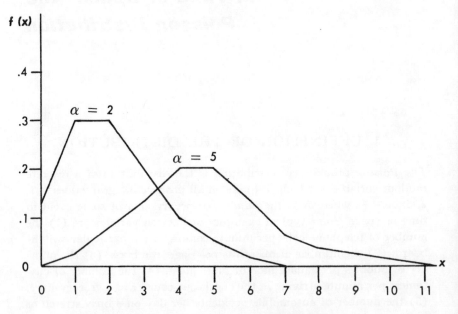

FIGURE 7-1. Poisson Probability Distribution for $\alpha = 2$ and $\alpha = 5$

substantially more advanced mathematics than the readers are assumed to have had.

As has already been indicated, X is a discrete random variable which can conceivably take on all nonnegative integer values, i.e., 0, 1, 2, 3, ... ∞. The Poisson density function gives the probability of occurrence of exactly X events within a given interval of time or space. In general, $P(X = x) = f(x)$ is positively skewed. That is, the function reaches its peak quickly as X takes on larger values and then decreases assymptotically toward zero. The exact nature of the distribution, however, depends on the value of α. The larger the value of α the larger must be the value of X before the density function reaches its peak. Figure 7–1 indicates the nature of $f(x)$ for two values of α. Values of $e^{-\alpha}$ for selected values of α are included in Appendix Table III. These can be used to calculate values of $f(x)$ by Equation 7–1, or more easily by Equation 7–2 below.

It should be noted that

$$\frac{f(x)}{f(x-1)} = \frac{\dfrac{\alpha^x e^{-\alpha}}{x!}}{\dfrac{\alpha^{x-1} e^{-\alpha}}{(x-1)!}} = \frac{\alpha}{x}.$$

Hence,

$$f(x) = \frac{\alpha}{x} f(x-1). \tag{7–2}$$

Using Equation 7–2, it is possible, given $f(0)$, to determine easily the value of the density function for all other values of X.

Example 7–1

Let us assume the value of α to be 1.0. Then

$$P(X = 0) = f(0) = e^{-\alpha} = e^{-1} = .3679 ,$$

$$f(1) = \frac{1}{1}(.3679) = .3679 ,$$

$$f(2) = \frac{1}{2}(.3679) = .18395 ,$$

$$f(3) = \frac{1}{3}(.18395) = .061317 ,$$

and so on. These values can be verified easily by reference to Appendix Table III.

7–2. THE EXPECTED VALUE OF X

As with the binomial and hypergeometric distributions, we may determine the expected value of the Poisson distributed variable X as follows:

$$E(X^2) = \sum_{x=0}^{\infty} x^2 \cdot f(x) = \sum_{x=0}^{\infty} x^2 \frac{\alpha^x e^{-\alpha}}{x!}. \qquad (7\text{–}3)$$

By a process of algebraic simplification, Equation 7–3 can be reduced to

$$E(X) = \alpha. \qquad (7\text{–}4)$$

Thus, the expected number of occurrences of an event within a given interval of time or space is α.

7–3. THE VARIANCE OF X

As with the other distributions that we have studied, the variance of the Poisson distributed variable is given by

$$\sigma^2 = E(X^2) - [E(X)]^2.$$

Substituting from Equation 7–4, we have

$$\sigma^2 = E(X^2) - \alpha^2. \qquad (7\text{–}5)$$

Let us look now at the first term on the right side of Equation 7–5. We have

$$E(X^2) = \sum_{x=0}^{\infty} x^2 \cdot f(x) = \sum_{x=0}^{\infty} x^2 \frac{\alpha^x e^{-\alpha}}{x!}. \qquad (7\text{–}6)$$

Now, Equation 7–6 can be reduced to

$$E(X^2) = \alpha^2 + \alpha. \qquad (7\text{–}7)$$

Substituting the results of Equation 7–7 into Equation 7–5, the variance becomes

$$\sigma^2 = \alpha^2 + \alpha - \alpha^2 = \alpha. \qquad (7\text{–}8)$$

Thus, the expected value and variance of the Poisson distributed variable are the same. The distribution has just one parameter, α. Given the value of α, the density function $f(x)$ is determined for all values of X.

Example 7–2

Suppose that we know from past records that on the average during a given period of the day the number of telephone calls coming into a particular switchboard per minute is three. The values of $f(x)$ for several possible values of X are:

x	$f(x)$
0	.0498
1	.1494
2	.2240
3	.2240
4	.1680
5	.1008
6	.0504
7	.0216
8	.0081
9	.0027
10	.0008
11	.0002
12	.0001

Suppose that the maximum number of calls that this switchboard can accommodate is six per minute. Then the probability that at least one caller will receive a busy signal during a given minute during this period is given by the sum of probabilities that X is equal to each of the integer values greater than six, namely,

$$P(X > 6) = \sum_{x=7}^{\infty} f(x) \cong .0335 .$$

7–4. SUMMARY OF DISCRETE PROBABILITY DISTRIBUTIONS

In these last three chapters we have discussed in some detail three basic discrete probability distributions: the hypergeometric, the binomial, and the Poisson distributions. It will be recalled that the hypergeometric distribution applies to problem situations where n elements are selected from a finite universe set of N elements without replacement between selections. The universe set is assumed to be divided into two subsets A and B. The hypergeometric density function, then, gives the probability of obtaining exactly x elements from subset A and $n - x$ from subset B. The problem situation leading to the binomial distribution is precisely the same as that leading to the hyper-geometric with the single exception that selections are made with replacement. The binomial distribution may also apply to problem situations where a series of independent selections or trials is made such that the probability of an event called "success" on each trial is p. The Poisson distribution is fundamentally different from each of the other two. Whereas they assume a sequence of selections or trials each of which may or may not result in a "success" (not more than one success can occur on a given trial), the Poisson distribution applies to problem situations in which some event occurs randomly over continuous time or space. It is shown in the more advanced studies of probability that the Poisson distribution may be used to give approximations to binomial probabilities if p is small and n large, where α is defined to be equal to $n \cdot p$. The chief characteristics of these three distributions are summarized in Figure 7–2.

Probability Distribution and Parameter Values	Probability Density Function and Range of Values of X	Mean or Expected Value $E(X) = \mu$	Variance σ^2
Hypergeometric $N = 1,2,\ldots$ $N_1 = 0,1,2,\ldots N$	$\dfrac{\dbinom{N_1}{x} \cdot \dbinom{N - N_1}{n - x}}{\dbinom{N}{n}}$ $x = 1,2,\ldots n$ if $n \leq N_1$ $x = 1,2,\ldots N_1$ if $n \geq N_1$	np where $p = N_1/N$	$npq\left(\dfrac{N - n}{N - 1}\right)$ where $p = N_1/N$
Binomial $n = 1,2,\ldots$ $0 \leq p \leq 1$	$\dbinom{n}{x} p^x q^{n-x}$ $x = 0,1,2,\ldots,n$	np	npq
Poisson $\alpha > 0$	$\dfrac{\alpha^x e^{-\alpha}}{x!}$ $x = 0, 1, 2,\ldots \infty$	α	α

FIGURE 7–2. Three Discrete Probability Distributions and Their Characteristics

Exercises

1. If a particular book has on the average one misprint per page, what is the probability that a page selected at random has more than two misprints?

(Ans. .08030)

2. On the basis of past experience, it is observed that a certain service station averages six customers per hour on holiday weekends. On a particular holiday weekend we will observe the number of customers arriving during a randomly selected one-hour period. What is the probability that no more than eight customers will arrive?

3. Suppose that a particular company operates a large fleet of trucks and that the number of breakdowns among the trucks per week follows a Poisson process with $\alpha = 7$. What is the probability that during a given week the number of breakdowns is (a) at least 10, (b) at least 9, (c) at least 8, (d) at least 7, (e) at least 6, (f) not more than 1, (g) not more than 2, (h) not more than 3?

4. On a typical day during the peak hours, 12 calls per hour come into **XYZ** Company's central telephone exchange. During a particular hour, what is the probability that fewer than 10 calls will be received? During a randomly selected 10-minute period, what is the probability that more than 3 calls will come into the exchange?

5. The quality control department of a manufacturer of light bulbs selects samples of 50 bulbs from lots of 1,000, and subjects them to a test. If in the test 2 or more are found to be defective, the whole lot is inspected 100 per cent and defective bulbs removed. Otherwise the lot passes inspection and is shipped out as is. If in fact 5 per cent of the bulbs in a given lot are defective, what is the probability that the lot will be shipped out without 100 per cent inspection?

6. Suppose that the average number of hurricanes per season in the Gulf of Mexico is four, and that the number of hurricanes per season is a Poisson process. What is the probability that in a given season there will be no hurricanes? What is the probability that there will be more than five?

(Ans. .01832; .23269)

7. Suppose that the service rate (number of automobile repairs completed per hour) in a particular automobile repair shop is 8 per hour. What is the probability that exactly 64 automobiles will be

repaired in a given 8-hour work day? What is the probability that more than 96 will be completed?

Selected References

Adams, J. K., *Basic Statistical Concepts,* New York: McGraw-Hill Book Company, Inc., 1956.

Feller, W., *Introduction to Probability Theory and Its Application,* Vol. I, 2nd. ed., New York: John Wiley & Sons, 1957.

Freund, J. E., *Mathematical Statistics,* Englewood Cliffs, N. J.: Prentice-Hall, Inc., 1962.

Hoel, P. G., *Introduction to Mathematical Statistics,* 2nd. ed., New York: John Wiley & Sons, 1954.

Meyer, P. L., *Introduction to Probability and Statistical Applications,* Reading, Mass.: Addison-Wesley Publishing Co., Inc., 1965.

Wadsworth, G. P., and J. G. Bryan, *Introduction to Probability and Random Variables,* New York: McGraw-Hill Book Company, Inc., 1960.

chapter eight

Some Applications of Probability Theory to Business and Related Problems

In the first chapter of this book we gave some indication of the nature of the chief problem of the modern business executive. His main function is to make decisions between alternative courses of action or policies to be carried out by the firm in the future, either the long-range future or the immediate future. However, the conditions under which these policies will be carried out are typically uncertain. For example, demands for the product of the firm, prices and availabilities of raw materials, wage rates that must be paid, climatic conditions and their effects on costs and work schedules, consumer preferences for alternative product designs, and so forth, are all uncertain in the future. All such decisions require either knowledge or assumptions about the many factors which will affect the outcome of whatever course of action is decided upon. As we have said, such *knowledge* is not available. Reliance on assumptions about these factors can be extremely dangerous. The various aspects of probability theory that

125

have been touched on here, however, can provide a basis on which analytical tools may be developed to use effectively such limited knowledge that is available so that sound decisions can be made.

Probability theory as studied here, moreover, is useful not only in business problems. It is useful in such widely diverse fields as experimental physics, biology, medicine, agricultural research, engineering, economics, etc. In fact, probability has been used effectively in virtually every field of study, and is the central core of the theory of statistics.

In all of the earlier chapters we have given many highly simplified examples of application of the various aspects of probability, both in the text itself and in the exercises at the end of the chapters. In this chapter we will attempt to give a somewhat more complete cataloging of the kinds of business and economic problems to which probability theory has been applied with considerable success.

8–1. INVENTORY CONTROL

One of the oldest and most highly developed applications of probability theory in business is in the development of inventory control models. These models are generally built up around two random processes. On the one hand, the demand for the product held in inventory is uncertain; it tends to fluctuate from period to period (the period may be a day, week, etc.) in a random manner. On the other hand, the time required to receive a replacement order into inventory is uncertain. The number of units of product demanded for a given period follows a discrete probability distribution, frequently the Poisson distribution. Time required for delivery of an order, however, follows a continuous distribution and cannot be represented by any of the distributions covered in this book.

The typical inventory model is a mathematical representation of the way in which variations in policies (on the number of units in each order placed to replenish inventory stock and the inventory level at which such orders are placed) affect the total cost associated with inventories. This cost is affected mainly by (1) the cost of acquiring goods, (2) the cost associated with placement of orders, (3) interest and related costs of holding items in inventory, and (4) costs resulting from running out of inventory and not being able to satisfy customer demand immediately. The first of these really has no effect unless quantity discounts or similar concessions are made for large orders. The second cost varies directly with the number of orders placed during a given span of time and inversely per unit ordered. The third cost varies directly with the average number of units held in inventory and inversely with the number of orders placed. Finally, the fourth cost tends to vary inversely with the average number of units held in inventory.

Given these four components of cost and the probability distributions describing fluctuations in number of units demanded per period and time required to receive an order, the model is then used to determine the order quantity and inventory level at the time the order is placed which will minimize the expected cost associated with inventories.

8–2. WAITING LINES

Related to inventory theory is the theory of waiting lines, or *queues*. As in inventory theory, queueing theory assumes two random processes. First, arrivals per period of time into a point of service of some sort are usually assumed to have a Poisson distribution. Second, the number of services completed per period at this point is also assumed to be Poisson distributed. Depending on the number of service facilities, on the relation between the rate of arrivals and the rate of services, and on assumptions about whether switching between service facilities is allowed, etc., the specific model can take many forms. Generally speaking, queueing models are designed and used to determine the optimum capacity of service facilities to minimize the overall cost of providing adequate service. Some examples of situations to which queueing theory applies are waiting lines at ticket windows (train tickets, theater tickets, plane tickets, etc.), airplanes waiting to land at an airport, ships or trucks waiting to unload at docks, people waiting at a barber shop or a beauty shop, taxis waiting at a taxi stand for a fare, messages waiting to be transmitted by cable, number of telephone calls coming into an exchange, people forming lines at a grocery check-out counter, people forming lines at a bank teller's window, cars forming lines at a toll booth, or mechanics in a shop forming lines at parts windows to get parts. In all such cases there is a need to provide sufficient capacity to serve the customers without their having to wait too long. At the same time, excess capacity involves an unnecessary cost. The purpose of the queueing model is to provide a means by which the optimum capacity can be determined (i.e., the capacity which minimizes the expected cost of providing adequate service).

8-3. EQUIPMENT MAINTENANCE AND REPLACEMENT

Similarly to inventory and queueing as discussed above, models have been developed to give an optimum solution to several variations on general equipment replacement and maintenance problems. The maintenance problem is one in which the time between breakdowns on individual machines (or components of a given machine) is a random process following either something like the Pascal distribution discussed in Chapter 6 (if time is treated in discrete intervals), or the exponential distribution (if time is treated as a continuous variable). The exponential distribution has not been covered in this book because it is a continuous distribution. However, it is derived from the Poisson distribution in much the same way as the Pascal distribution is derived from the binomial. (This is the same distribution which is usually used in inventory theory for the time required for a delivery.) Given the distribution between breakdowns, the objective of the maintenance problem is to determine a preventive maintenance policy so as to minimize the total cost of maintenance including down time.

In general, there are two classes of equipment replacement problems. One is such that the old equipment gradually becomes less efficient with increasing age. Possibly the increased age leads to increased probability of breakdown during a given period so that maintenance cost increases over time. Or perhaps the cost of operating the equipment increases over time. In either case the objective is to determine an optimum replacement interval. The second class of replacement problems is such that the equipment continues to operate at more or less equal efficiency until it fails without warning. An example is light bulbs. The failure rate is usually assumed to follow a Poisson probability distribution. The aim of the model is to determine an optimum replacement policy: whether it is cheaper to replace items as they fail or to replace groups of them at periodic intervals, and what the optimum replacement interval is.

8-4. INDUSTRIAL QUALITY CONTROL

A very old use of probability theory in business is in the control of quality in manufacturing processes. Many of our examples and exercises in almost all of the chapters of the book have been drawn from quality control. The quality of virtually all manufactured products in this country is controlled by application of probability theory. Suppose, for example, that we have a manufacturing process which is supposed to turn out ball bearings with no more than one-half per cent defective bearings. In order to judge whether or not the process is operating according to standard, we select at random 100 bearings and inspect them. If the process is "in control" the probability of getting more than 2 defective bearings in our sample is only .0144. That is, occurrence of more than 2 defects would be a very rare event if the process is "in control." Hence, if we do get more than 2 defective bearings, we are led to conclude that the process is not operating according to standard; it is "out of control." This means that something must be wrong and we should find out what it is.

8–5. STATISTICAL APPLICATIONS

Probability theory serves as the central core of all of the modern theory of statistics. The statement applies particularly to the theory of probability distributions. Statistical theory in turn provides the means by which generalizations can be made about a whole class of real life situations on the basis of a very limited number of observations. For example, suppose that we are selecting a few elements from a universe set S which we believe to be partitioned into two subsets A and B. However, we do not know the proportion of the elements in the universe set which are in A and the proportion which are in B. On the basis of some very powerful statistical theory, we can draw conclusions about this proportion which we can say, with a specified probability, are correct. By proper and careful application of this theory we may be able to predict accurately the outcome of an election, to determine whether consumers will prefer one new product design or package design to another, to decide which of several alternative advertising lay-outs is most effective, to determine whether or not a new drug is more effective in curing a particular disease than another, to determine which of several alternative formulas of agricultural fertilizer is most effective in a particular area, to forecast accurately the demand for a new product or the level of national income next year, and so on. Statistical theory provides a means by which we can draw important conclusions about conditions existing in the world (present or future) on the basis of very limited information. However, as already indicated, modern statistical theory is entirely dependent upon probability theory, without which it could never have developed.

8–6. ALLOWANCE FOR BAD DEBTS AMONG DEPARTMENT STORE ACCOUNTS

One very interesting use of probability theory to the solution of a very common practical problem was the application (by Professors Cyert, Davidson, and Thompson of Carnegie Institute of Technology) of the theory of Markov chains (as introduced in Chapter 3) to estimate the optimum allowance for bad debts for a large department store.[1] In this study, the charge accounts of a large department store were analyzed in detail. Accounts were classified by age of account according to the number of payment periods past due. For each payment period a record was made as to the changes in age classification between consecutive periods. These data were used to determine the probabilities of making the transition from each age classification to each other one between periods. These probabilities, and the dollar amounts of accounts receivable in each category were then used to estimate (by Markov chain theory) loss expectancy rates by age of accounts, an optimum allowance for doubtful accounts, and several other measures.

8–7. SOME OTHER APPLICATIONS

In addition to the sorts of applications which have been mentioned so far in this chapter, there are many more special cases which will not be mentioned here. A few other applications to business and economic problems, however, should at least be mentioned. For example, although we have not mentioned it in this chapter, we have taken up earlier the application of the notion of mathematical expectation as a means of guiding decisions between two or more alternative courses of action. This is a very general approach to a problem. It can be used effectively to choose between two or more alternative inventory policies, to decide which of two or more possible locations for a retail store would be most profitable (assuming sufficient knowledge of the probabilities of success in each of the locations), to decide whether or not an expensive quality control system is worthwhile, to decide which of two or more preventive maintenance policies is least costly over time, to decide which (if any) of several contracts is to be bid on by construction firms, and many more.

---

[1]R. M. Cyert, H. J. Davidson, and G. L. Thompson, "Estimation of the Allowance for Doubtful Accounts by Markov Chains," *Management Science* (April, 1962), pp. 287-303.

In economics much work has been done in recent years toward the use of probability models in the explanation and prediction of the levels of economic activity and the kinds of activity carried out. These models have been used to predict such things as gross national product and national income, capital investment, consumer expenditures, total employment, and employment by industry, among other things for the national economy. Moreover, somewhat similar models have been developed and applied (generally, though with somewhat less success than the national models) for the economies of small areas and regions.

Other economists have used probability theory (mainly the theory of Markov chains) to study the problem of industrial concentration. The purpose has been two-fold: to develop more adequate measures of monopoly power than those previously available, and to analyze variations in industrial concentration and mobility of firms in and out of American industry with the hope of predicting the trend of concentration in the future. Over the years there have been almost continual discussions among economists as to whether our economy has become more or less competitive in recent times. However, most economists have agreed that there have been no adequate measures of the extent of competition at a given time, or changes in the extent of competition over time. Hence, none of the arguments on either side of the question could be supported adequately. The use of Markov chain theory has not solved the problem completely but it has contributed significantly to its solution.

Recently there have been several applications of probability models in the analysis of population mobility. These have been used in an effort to forecast for future periods migration rates in or out of small areas and to estimate population growth of small areas. This work, however, has been of an experimental nature and as yet its reliability has not been well established.

8–8. SOME CONCLUDING COMMENTS

In this book we have presented the main body of elementary probability theory for finite sample spaces. Although there is much that has not been covered here, we have tried to give an accurate treatment of what has been covered, but to do so in such a way that it would be clear to the student. In the process of discussing the subject matter we have tried at all times to illustrate by realistic, though highly simplified, examples. Most of you will probably take several more courses over the next few years in which much, if not most, of the material covered here can be applied to the same sorts of problems discussed in this book.

Selected References

Goetz, B. E., *Quantitative Methods*, New York: McGraw-Hill Book Company, Inc., 1965.

Kemeny, J. G., A. Schleifer, J. L. Snell, and G. L. Thompson, *Finite Mathematics with Business Applications*, Englewood Cliffs, N. J.: Prentice-Hall, Inc., 1962.

Levin, R. I., and C. A. Kirkpatrick, *Quantitative Approaches to Management*, New York: McGraw-Hill Book Company, Inc., 1965.

Sesieni, M., A. Yaspan, and L. Friedman, *Operations Research — Methods and Problems*, New York: John Wiley & Sons, Inc., 1959.

Theil, H., J. C. G. Boot, and T. Kloek, *Operations Research and Quantitative Economics*, New York: McGraw-Hill Book Company, Inc., 1965.

Appendix
and
Index

TABLE I
Combinatorial Values*

n	0	1	2	3	4	5	6	7	8	9	10
1	1	1									
2	1	2	1								
3	1	3	3	1							
4	1	4	6	4	1						
5	1	5	10	10	5	1					
6	1	6	15	20	15	6	1				
7	1	7	21	35	35	21	7	1			
8	1	8	28	56	70	56	28	8	1		
9	1	9	36	84	126	126	84	36	9	1	
10	1	10	45	120	210	252	210	120	45	10	1
11	1	11	55	165	330	462	462	330	165	55	11
12	1	12	66	220	495	792	924	792	495	220	66
13	1	13	78	286	715	1287	1716	1716	1287	715	286
14	1	14	91	364	1001	2002	3003	3432	3003	2002	1001
15	1	15	105	455	1365	3003	5005	5435	6435	5005	3003
16	1	16	120	560	1820	4368	8008	11440	12870	11440	8008
17	1	17	136	680	2380	6188	12376	19448	24310	24310	19448
18	1	18	153	816	3060	8568	18564	31824	43758	48620	43758
19	1	19	171	969	3876	11628	27132	50388	75582	92378	92378
20	1	20	190	1140	4845	15504	38760	77520	125970	167960	184756

n	11	12	13	14	15	16	17	18	19	20
1										
2										
3										
4										
5										
6										
7										
8										
9										
10										
11	1									
12	12	1								
13	78	13	1							
14	364	91	14	1						
15	1365	455	105	15	1					
16	4368	1820	560	120	16	1				
17	12376	6188	2380	680	136	17	1			
18	31824	18564	8568	3060	816	153	18	1		
19	75582	50388	27132	11628	3876	969	171	19	1	
20	167960	125970	77520	38760	15504	4845	1140	190	20	1

*Values in the table are given by $\binom{n}{x}$ for all integer values of x such that $0 \leq x \leq n$.

135

TABLE II
Binomial Probabilities*

n	x	.05	.10	.15	.20	.25	.30	.35	.40	.45	.50
						p					
1	0	.9500	.9000	.8500	.8000	.7500	.7000	.6500	.6000	.5500	.5000
	1	.0500	.1000	.1500	.2000	.2500	.3000	.3500	.4000	.4500	.5000
2	0	.9025	.8100	.7225	.6400	.5625	.4900	.4225	.3600	.3025	.2500
	1	.0950	.1800	.2550	.3200	.3750	.4200	.4550	.4800	.4950	.5000
	2	.0025	.0100	.0225	.0400	.0625	.0900	.1225	.1600	.2025	.2500
3	0	.8574	.7290	.6141	.5120	.4219	.3430	.2746	.2160	.1664	.1250
	1	.1354	.2430	.3251	.3840	.4219	.4410	.4436	.4320	.4084	.3750
	2	.0071	.0270	.0574	.0960	.1406	.1890	.2389	.2880	.3341	.3750
	3	.0001	.0010	.0034	.0080	.0156	.0270	.0429	.0640	.0911	.1250
4	0	.8145	.6561	.5220	.4096	.3164	.2401	.1785	.1296	.0915	.0625
	1	.1715	.2916	.3685	.4096	.4219	.4116	.3845	.3456	.2995	.2500
	2	.0135	.0486	.0975	.1536	.2109	.2646	.3105	.3456	.3675	.3750
	3	.0005	.0036	.0115	.0256	.0469	.0756	.1115	.1536	.2005	.2500
	4	.0000	.0001	.0005	.0016	.0039	.0081	.0150	.0256	.0410	.0625
5	0	.7738	.5905	.4437	.3277	.2373	.1681	.1160	.0778	.0503	.0312
	1	.2036	.3280	.3915	.4096	.3955	.3602	.3124	.2592	.2059	.1562
	2	.0214	.0729	.1382	.2048	.2637	.3087	.3364	.3456	.3369	.3125
	3	.0011	.0081	.0244	.0512	.0879	.1323	.1811	.2304	.2757	.3125
	4	.0000	.0004	.0022	.0064	.0146	.0284	.0488	.0768	.1128	.1562
	5	.0000	.0000	.0001	.0003	.0010	.0024	.0053	.0102	.0185	.0312
6	0	.7351	.5314	.3771	.2621	.1780	.1176	.0754	.0467	.0277	.0156
	1	.2321	.3543	.3993	.3932	.3560	.3025	.2437	.1866	.1359	.0938
	2	.0305	.0984	.1762	.2458	.2966	.3241	.3280	.3110	.2780	.2344
	3	.0021	.0146	.0415	.0819	.1318	.1852	.2355	.2765	.3032	.3125
	4	.0001	.0012	.0055	.0154	.0330	.0595	.0951	.1382	.1861	.2344
	5	.0000	.0001	.0004	.0015	.0044	.0102	.0205	.0369	.0609	.0938
	6	.0000	.0000	.0000	.0001	.0002	.0007	.0018	.0041	.0083	.0516'
7	0	.6983	.4783	.3206	.2097	.1335	.0824	.0490	.0280	.0152	.0078
	1	.2573	.3720	.3960	.3670	.3115	.2471	.1848	.1306	.0872	.0547
	2	.0406	.1240	.2097	.2753	.3115	.3177	.2985	.2613	.2140	.1641
	3	.0036	.0230	.0617	.1147	.1730	.2269	.2679	.2903	.2918	.2734
	4	.0002	.0026	.0109	.0287	.0577	.0972	.1442	.1935	.2388	.2734
	5	.0009	.0002	.0012	.0043	.0115	.0250	.0466	.0774	.1172	.1641
	6	.0000	.0000	.0001	.0004	.0013	.0036	.0084	.0172	.0320	.0547
	7	.0000	.0000	.0000	.0000	.0001	.0002	.0006	.0016	.0037	.0078
8	0	.6634	.4305	.2725	.1678	.1001	.0576	.0319	.0168	.0084	.0039
	1	.2793	.3826	.3847	.3355	.2670	.1977	.1373	.0896	.0548	.0312
	2	.0515	.1488	.2376	.2936	.3115	.2965	.2587	.2090	.1569	.1094
	3	.0054	.0331	.0839	.1468	.2076	.2541	.2786	.2787	.2568	.2188
	4	.0004	.0046	.0815	.0459	.0865	.1361	.1875	.2322	.2627	.2734

*Taken from National Bureau of Standards, U.S. Department of Commerce, *Tables of the Binomial Probability Distribution,* Applied Mathematics Series 6 (Washington, D. C.: U.S. Government Printing Office, 1949).

n	x	.05	.10	.15	.20	p .25	.30	.35	.40	.45	.50
	5	.0000	.0004	.0026	.0092	.0231	.0467	.0808	.1239	.1719	.2188
	6	.0000	.0000	.0002	.0011	.0038	.0100	.0217	.0413	.0703	.1094
	7	.0000	.0000	.0000	.0001	.0004	.0012	.0033	.0079	.0164	.0312
	8	.0000	.0000	.0000	.0000	.0000	.0001	.0002	.0007	.0017	.0039
9	0	.6302	.3874	.2316	.1342	.0751	.0404	.0207	.0101	.0046	.0020
	1	.2985	.3874	.3679	.3020	.2253	.1556	.1004	.0605	.0339	.0176
	2	.0629	.1722	.2597	.3020	.3003	.2668	.2162	.1612	.1110	.0703
	3	.0077	.0446	.1069	.1762	.2336	.2668	.2716	.2508	.2119	.1641
	4	.0006	.0074	.0283	.0661	.1168	.1715	.2194	.2508	.2600	.2461
	5	.0000	.0008	.0050	.0165	.0389	.0735	.1181	.1672	.2128	.2461
	6	.0000	.0001	.0006	.0028	.0087	.0210	.0424	.0743	.1160	.1641
	7	.0000	.0000	.0000	.0003	.0012	.0039	.0098	.0212	.0407	.0703
	8	.0000	.0000	.0000	.0000	.0001	.0004	.0013	.0035	.0083	.0716
	9	.0000	.0000	.0000	.0000	.0000	.0000	.0001	.0003	.0008	.0020
10	0	.5987	.3487	.1969	.1074	.0563	.0282	.0135	.0060	.0025	.0010
	1	.3151	.3874	.3474	.2684	.1877	.1211	.0725	.0403	.0207	.0098
	2	.0746	.1937	.2759	.3020	.2816	.2335	.1757	.1209	.0763	.0439
	3	.0105	.0574	.1298	.2013	.2503	.2668	.2522	.2150	.1665	.1172
	4	.0010	.0112	.0401	.0881	.1460	.2001	.2377	.2508	.2384	.2051
	5	.0001	.0015	.0085	.0264	.0584	.1029	.1536	.2007	.2340	.2461
	6	.0000	.0001	.0012	.0055	.0162	.0368	.0689	.1115	.1596	.2051
	7	.0000	.0000	.0001	.0008	.0031	.0090	.0212	.0425	.0746	.1172
	8	.0000	.0000	.0000	.0001	.0004	.0014	.0043	.0106	.0229	.0439
	9	.0000	.0000	.0000	.0000	.0000	.0001	.0005	.0016	.0042	.0098
	10	.0000	.0000	.0000	.0000	.0000	.0000	.0000	.0001	.0003	.0010
11	0	.5688	.3138	.1673	.0859	.0422	.0198	.0088	.0036	.0014	.0005
	1	.3293	.3835	.3248	.2362	.1549	.0932	.0518	.0266	.0125	.0054
	2	.0867	.2131	.2866	.2953	.2581	.1998	.1395	.0887	.0513	.0269
	3	.0137	.0710	.1517	.2215	.2581	.2568	.2254	.1774	.1259	.0806
	4	.0014	.0158	.0536	.1107	.1721	.2201	.2428	.2365	.2060	.1611
	5	.0001	.0025	.0132	.0388	.0803	.1321	.1830	.2207	.2360	.2256
	6	.0000	.0003	.0023	.0097	.0268	.0566	.0985	.1471	.1931	.2256
	7	.0000	.0000	.0003	.0017	.0064	.0173	.0379	.0701	.1128	.1611
	8	.0000	.0000	.0000	.0002	.0011	.0037	.0102	.0234	.0462	.0806
	9	.0000	.0000	.0000	.0000	.0001	.0005	.0018	.0052	.0126	.0269
	10	.0000	.0000	.0000	.0000	.0000	.0000	.0002	.0007	.0021	.0054
	11	.0000	.0000	.0000	.0000	.0000	.0000	.0000	.0000	.0002	.0005
12	0	.5404	.2824	.1422	.0687	.0317	.0138	.0057	.0022	.0008	.0002
	1	.3413	.3766	.3012	.2062	.1267	.0712	.0368	.0174	.0075	.0029
	2	.0988	.2301	.2924	.2835	.2323	.1678	.1088	.0639	.0339	.0161
	3	.0173	.0852	.1720	.2362	.2581	.2397	.1954	.1419	.0923	.0537
	4	.0021	.0213	.0683	.1329	.1936	.2311	.2367	.2128	.1700	.1208
	5	.0002	.0038	.0193	.0532	.1032	.1585	.2039	.2270	.2225	.1934
	6	.0000	.0005	.0040	.0155	.0401	.0792	.1281	.1766	.2124	.2256
	7	.0000	.0000	.0006	.0033	.0115	.0291	.0591	.1009	.1489	.1934
	8	.0000	.0000	.0001	.0005	.0024	.0078	.0199	.0420	.0762	.1208
	9	.0000	.0000	.0000	.0001	.0004	.0015	.0048	.0125	.0277	.0537

n	x	.05	.10	.15	.20	.25	.30	.35	.40	.45	.50
						p					
	10	.0000	.0000	.0000	.0000	.0000	.0002	.0008	.0025	.0068	.0161
	11	.0000	.0000	.0000	.0000	.0000	.0000	.0001	.0003	.0010	.0029
	12	.0000	.0000	.0000	.0000	.0000	.0000	.0000	.0000	.0001	.0002
13	0	.5133	.2542	.1209	.0550	.0238	.0097	.0037	.0013	.0004	.0001
	1	.3512	.3672	.2774	.1787	.1029	.0540	.0259	.0113	.0045	.0016
	2	.1109	.2448	.2937	.2680	.2059	.1388	.0836	.0453	.0220	.0095
	3	.0214	.0997	.1900	.2457	.2517	.2181	.1651	.1107	.0660	.0349
	4	.0028	.0277	.0838	.1535	.2097	.2337	.2222	.1845	.1350	.0873
	5	.0003	.0055	.0266	.0691	.1258	.1803	.2154	.2214	.1989	.1571
	6	.0000	.0008	.0063	.0230	.0559	.1030	.1546	.1968	.2169	.2095
	7	.0000	.0001	.0011	.0058	.0186	.0442	.0833	.1312	.1775	.2095
	8	.0000	.0000	.0001	.0011	.0047	.0142	.0336	.0656	.1089	.1571
	9	.0000	.0000	.0000	.0001	.0009	.0034	.0101	.0243	.0495	.0873
	10	.0000	.0000	.0000	.0000	.0001	.0006	.0022	.0065	.0162	.0349
	11	.0000	.0000	.0000	.0000	.0000	.0001	.0003	.0012	.0036	.0095
	12	.0000	.0000	.0000	.0000	.0000	.0000	.0000	.0001	.0005	.0016
	13	.0000	.0000	.0000	.0000	.0000	.0000	.0000	.0000	.0000	.0001
14	0	.4877	.2288	.1028	.0440	.0178	.0068	.0024	.0008	.0002	.0001
	1	.3593	.3559	.2539	.1539	.0832	.0407	.0181	.0073	.0027	.0009
	2	.1229	.2570	.2912	.2501	.1802	.1134	.0634	.0317	.0141	.0056
	3	.0259	.1142	.2056	.2501	.2402	.1943	.1366	.0845	.0462	.0222
	4	.0037	.0348	.0998	.1720	.2202	.2290	.2022	.1549	.1040	.0611
	5	.0004	.0078	.0352	.0860	.1468	.1963	.2178	.2066	.1701	.1222
	6	.0000	.0013	.0093	.0322	.0734	.1262	.1759	.2066	.2088	.1833
	7	.0000	.0002	.0019	.0092	.0280	.0618	.1082	.1574	.1952	.2095
	8	.0000	.0000	.0003	.0020	.0082	.0232	.0510	.0918	.1398	.1833
	9	.0000	.0000	.0000	.0003	.0018	.0066	.0183	.0408	.0762	.1222
	10	.0000	.0000	.0000	.0000	.0003	.0014	.0049	.0136	.0312	.0611
	11	.0000	.0000	.0000	.0000	.0000	.0002	.0010	.0033	.0093	.0222
	12	.0000	.0000	.0000	.0000	.0000	.0000	.0001	.0005	.0019	.0056
	13	.0000	.0000	.0000	.0000	.0000	.0000	.0000	.0001	.0002	.0009
	14	.0000	.0000	.0000	.0000	.0000	.0000	.0000	.0000	.0000	.0001
15	0	.4633	.2059	.0874	.0352	.0134	.0047	.0016	.0005	.0001	.0000
	1	.3658	.3432	.2312	.1319	.0668	.0305	.0126	.0047	.0016	.0005
	2	.1348	.2669	.2856	.2309	.1559	.0916	.0476	.0219	.0090	.0032
	3	.0307	.1285	.2184	.2501	.2252	.1700	.1110	.0634	.0318	.0139
	4	.0049	.0428	.1156	.1876	.2252	.2186	.1792	.1268	.0780	.0417
	5	.0006	.0105	.0449	.1032	.1651	.2061	.2123	.1859	.1404	.0916
	6	.0000	.0019	.0132	.0430	.0917	.1472	.1906	.2066	.1914	.1527
	7	.0000	.0003	.0030	.0138	.0393	.0811	.1319	.1771	.2013	.1964
	8	.0000	.0000	.0005	.0035	.0131	.0348	.0710	.1181	.1647	.1964
	9	.0000	.0000	.0001	.0007	.0034	.0116	.0298	.0612	.1048	.1527
	10	.0000	.0000	.0000	.0001	.0007	.0030	.0096	.0245	.0515	.0916
	11	.0000	.0000	.0000	.0000	.0001	.0006	.0024	.0074	.0191	.0417
	12	.0000	.0000	.0000	.0000	.0000	.0001	.0004	.0016	.0052	.0139
	13	.0000	.0000	.0000	.0000	.0000	.0000	.0001	.0003	.0010	.0032
	14	.0000	.0000	.0000	.0000	.0000	.0000	.0000	.0000	.0001	.0005

n	x	.05	.10	.15	.20	p .25	.30	.35	.40	.45	.50
	15	.0000	.0000	.0000	.0000	.0000	.0000	.0000	.0000	.0000	.0000
16	0	.4401	.1853	.0743	.0281	.0100	.0033	.0010	.0003	.0001	.0000
	1	.3706	.3294	.2097	.1126	.0535	.0228	.0087	.0030	.0009	.0002
	2	.1463	.2745	.2775	.2111	.1336	.0732	.0353	.0150	.0056	.0018
	3	.0359	.1423	.2285	.2463	.2079	.1465	.0888	.0468	.0215	.0085
	4	.0061	.0514	.1311	.2001	.2252	.2040	.1553	.1014	.0572	.0278
	5	.0008	.0137	.0555	.1201	.1802	.2099	.2008	.1623	.1123	.0667
	6	.0001	.0028	.0180	.0550	.1101	.1649	.1982	.1983	.1684	.1222
	7	.0000	.0004	.0045	.0197	.0524	.1010	.1524	.1889	.1969	.1746
	8	.0000	.0001	.0009	.0055	.0197	.0487	.0923	.1417	.1812	.1964
	9	.0000	.0000	.0001	.0012	.0058	.0185	.0442	.0840	.1318	.1746
	10	.0000	.0000	.0000	.0002	.0014	.0056	.0167	.0392	.0755	.1222
	11	.0000	.0000	.0000	.0000	.0002	.0013	.0049	.0142	.0337	.0667
	12	.0000	.0000	.0000	.0000	.0000	.0002	.0011	.0040	.0115	.0278
	13	.0000	.0000	.0000	.0000	.0000	.0000	.0002	.0008	.0029	.0085
	14	.0000	.0000	.0000	.0000	.0000	.0000	.0000	.0001	.0005	.0018
	15	.0000	.0000	.0000	.0000	.0000	.0000	.0000	.0000	.0001	.0002
	16	.0000	.0000	.0000	.0000	.0000	.0000	.0000	.0000	.0000	.0000
17	0	.4181	.1668	.0631	.0225	.0075	.0023	.0007	.0002	.0000	.0000
	1	.3741	.3150	.1893	.0957	.0426	.0169	.0060	.0019	.0005	.0001
	2	.1575	.2800	.2673	.1914	.1136	.0581	.0260	.0102	.0035	.0010
	3	.0415	.1556	.2359	.2393	.1893	.1245	.0701	.0341	.0144	.0052
	4	.0076	.0605	.1457	.2093	.2209	.1868	.1320	.0796	.0411	.0182
	5	.0010	.0175	.0668	.1361	.1914	.2081	.1849	.1379	.0875	.0472
	6	.0001	.0039	.0236	.0680	.1276	.1784	.1991	.1839	.1432	.0944
	7	.0000	.0007	.0065	.0267	.0668	.1201	.1685	.1927	.1841	.1484
	8	.0000	.0001	.0014	.0084	.0279	.0644	.1134	.1606	.1883	.1855
	9	.0000	.0000	.0003	.0021	.0093	.0276	.0611	.1070	.1540	.1855
	10	.0000	.0000	.0000	.0004	.0025	.0095	.0263	.0571	.1008	.1484
	11	.0000	.0000	.0000	.0001	.0005	.0026	.0090	.0242	.0525	.0944
	12	.0000	.0000	.0000	.0000	.0001	.0006	.0024	.0021	.0215	.0472
	13	.0000	.0000	.0000	.0000	.0000	.0001	.0005	.0021	.0068	.0182
	14	.0000	.0000	.0000	.0000	.0000	.0000	.0001	.0004	.0016	.0052
	15	.0000	.0000	.0000	.0000	.0000	.0000	.0000	.0001	.0003	.0010
	16	.0000	.0000	.0000	.0000	.0000	.0000	.0000	.0000	.0000	.0001
	17	.0000	.0000	.0000	.0000	.0000	.0000	.0000	.0000	.0000	.0000
18	0	.3972	.1501	.0536	.0180	.0056	.0016	.0004	.0001	.0000	.0000
	1	.3763	.3002	.1704	.0811	.0338	.0126	.0042	.0012	.0003	.0001
	2	.1683	.2835	.2556	.1723	.0958	.0458	.0190	.0069	.0022	.0006
	3	.0473	.1680	.2406	.2297	.1704	.1046	.0547	.0246	.0095	.0031
	4	.0093	.0700	.1592	.2153	.2130	.1681	.1104	.0614	.0291	.0117
	5	.0014	.0218	.0787	.1507	.1988	.2017	.1664	.1146	.0666	.0327
	6	.0002	.0052	.0301	.0816	.1436	.1873	.1941	.1655	.1181	.0708
	7	.0000	.0010	.0091	.0350	.0820	.1376	.1792	.1892	.1657	.1214
	8	.0000	.0002	.0022	.0120	.0376	.0811	.1327	.1734	.1864	.1669
	9	.0000	.0000	.0004	.0033	.0139	.0386	.0794	.1284	.1694	.1855

n	x	.05	.10	.15	.20	p .25	.30	.35	.40	.45	.50
	10	.0000	.0000	.0001	.0008	.0042	.0149	.0385	.0771	.1248	.1669
	11	.0000	.0000	.0000	.0001	.0010	.0046	.0151	.0374	.0742	.1214
	12	.0000	.0000	.0000	.0000	.0002	.0012	.0047	.0145	.0354	.0708
	13	.0000	.0000	.0000	.0000	.0000	.0002	.0012	.0044	.0134	.0327
	14	.0000	.0000	.0000	.0000	.0000	.0000	.0002	.0011	.0039	.0117
	15	.0000	.0000	.0000	.0000	.0000	.0000	.0000	.0002	.0009	.0031
	16	.0000	.0000	.0000	.0000	.0000	.0000	.0000	.0000	.0001	.0006
	17	.0000	.0000	.0000	.0000	.0000	.0000	.0000	.0000	.0000	.0001
	18	.0000	.0000	.0000	.0000	.0000	.0000	.0000	.0000	.0000	.0000
19	0	.3774	.1351	.0456	.0144	.0042	.0011	.0003	.0001	.0000	.0000
	1	.3774	.2852	.1529	.0685	.0268	.0093	.0029	.0008	.0002	.0000
	2	.1787	.2852	.2428	.1540	.0803	.0358	.0138	.0046	.0013	.0003
	3	.0533	.1796	.2428	.2182	.1517	.0869	.0422	.0175	.0062	.0018
	4	.0112	.0798	.1714	.2182	.2023	.1491	.0909	.0467	.0203	.0074
	5	.0018	.0266	.0907	.1636	.2023	.1916	.1468	.0933	.0497	.0222
	6	.0002	.0069	.0374	.0955	.1574	.1916	.1844	.1451	.0949	.0518
	7	.0000	.0014	.0122	.0443	.0974	.1525	.1844	.1797	.1443	.0961
	8	.0000	.0002	.0032	.0166	.0487	.0981	.1489	.1797	.1771	.1442
	9	.0000	.0000	.0007	.0051	.0198	.0514	.0980	.1464	.1771	.1762
	10	.0000	.0000	.0001	.0013	.0066	.0220	.0528	.0976	.1449	.1762
	11	.0000	.0000	.0000	.0003	.0018	.0077	.0233	.0532	.0970	.1442
	12	.0000	.0000	.0000	.0000	.0004	.0022	.0083	.0237	.0529	.0961
	13	.0000	.0000	.0000	.0000	.0001	.0005	.0024	.0085	.0233	.0518
	14	.0000	.0000	.0000	.0000	.0000	.0001	.0006	.0024	.0082	.0222
	15	.0000	.0000	.0000	.0000	.0000	.0000	.0001	.0005	.0022	.0074
	16	.0000	.0000	.0000	.0000	.0000	.0000	.0000	.0001	.0005	.0018
	17	.0000	.0000	.0000	.0000	.0000	.0000	.0000	.0000	.0001	.0003
	18	.0000	.0000	.0000	.0000	.0000	.0000	.0000	.0000	.0000	.0000
	19	.0000	.0000	.0000	.0000	.0000	.0000	.0000	.0000	.0000	.0000
20	0	.3585	.1216	.0388	.0115	.0032	.0008	.0002	.0000	.0000	.0000
	1	.3774	.2702	.1368	.0576	.0211	.0068	.0020	.0005	.0001	.0000
	2	.1887	.2852	.2293	.1369	.0669	.0278	.0100	.0031	.0008	.0002
	3	.0596	.1901	.2428	.2054	.1339	.0716	.0323	.0123	.0040	.0011
	4	.0133	.0898	.1821	.2182	.1897	.1304	.0738	.0350	.0139	.0046
	5	.0022	.0319	.1028	.1746	.2023	.1789	.1272	.0746	.0365	.0148
	6	.0003	.0089	.0454	.1091	.1686	.1916	.1712	.1244	.0746	.0370
	7	.0000	.0020	.0160	.0545	.1124	.1643	.1844	.1659	.1221	.0739
	8	.0000	.0004	.0046	.0222	.0609	.1144	.1614	.1797	.1623	.1201
	9	.0000	.0001	.0011	.0074	.0271	.0654	.1158	.1597	.1771	.1602
	10	.0000	.0000	.0002	.0020	.0099	.0308	.0686	.1171	.1593	.1762
	11	.0000	.0000	.0000	.0005	.0030	.0120	.0336	.0710	.1185	.1602
	12	.0000	.0000	.0000	.0001	.0008	.0039	.0136	.0355	.0727	.1201
	13	.0000	.0000	.0000	.0000	.0002	.0010	.0045	.0146	.0366	.0739
	14	.0000	.0000	.0000	.0000	.0000	.0002	.0012	.0049	.0150	.0370
	15	.0000	.0000	.0000	.0000	.0000	.0000	.0003	.0013	.0049	.0148
	16	.0000	.0000	.0000	.0000	.0000	.0000	.0000	.0003	.0013	.0046

n	x	.05	.10	.15	.20	p .25	.30	.35	.40	.45	.50
	17	.0000	.0000	.0000	.0000	.0000	.0000	.0000	.0000	.0002	.0011
	18	.0000	.0000	.0000	.0000	.0000	.0000	.0000	.0000	.0000	.0002
	19	.0000	.0000	.0000	.0000	.0000	.0000	.0000	.0000	.0000	.0000
	20	.0000	.0000	.0000	.0000	.0000	.0000	.0000	.0000	.0000	.0000

TABLE III
Values of the Negative Exponential $e^{-\alpha}$*

α	$e^{-\alpha}$
.1	.90484
.2	.81873
.3	.74082
.4	.67032
.5	.60653
.6	.54881
.7	.49659
.8	.44933
.9	.40657
1.0	.36788
1.1	.33287
1.2	.30119
1.3	.27253
1.4	.24660
1.5	.22313
1.6	.20190
1.7	.18268
1.8	.16530
1.9	.14957
2.0	.13534
2.1	.12246
2.2	.11080
2.3	.10026
2.4	.09071
3.0	.04979
4.0	.01832
5.0	.00674
6.0	.00248
7.0	.00091
8.0	.00034
9.0	.00012
10.0	.00005
11.0	.00002
12.0	.00001
13.0	.00000

*Taken from National Bureau of Standards, U.S. Department of Commerce, *Tables of the Exponential Function* e^x, Applied Mathematics Series 14, (Washington, D. C.: U.S. Government Printing Office, 1951).

Index